THE ILLUSTRATED NATURAL HISTORY OF CANADA

Scientific Consultants to the Series

The Atlantic Coast FRANKLIN RUSSELL

Earth Science Consultant WALTER TOVELL, Curator, Department of Geology, Royal Ontario Museum. *Life Science Consultant* J. MURRAY SPEIRS, Department of Zoology, University of Toronto

Library of Congress Catalog Card Number: 70-109048

N.S.L. Natural Science of Canada Limited
58 Northline Road, Toronto 16, Ontario, Canada

Publisher: Jack McClelland
Managing Editor: Michael Worek
Assistant Editor: Dorothy Martins
Art Director: William Fox
Visual Editor: Bill Brooks

Editorial Consultant: Pierre Berton

THE ATLANTIC COAST

Art Director: William Fox
Artists: Vlasta van Kampen /
Gordon McLean / Jerry Kozoriz /
Tom McNeely / Bill Henry / Gus Fantuz

Page 1: A baby seal contentedly snuggling in the snow.
Page 2/3: Rays from a golden sun shine through the mist at Cole Harbour, Nova Scotia.
Page 4/5: Massing together on Funk Island, murres smother the landscape.

Contents

Prologue

The author on a field trip to the Atlantic region.

A WEALTH OF SIGHT AND SOUND

In December, 1497, Raimondo de Soncino, an Italian living in London, wrote to the Duke of Milan about a land across the Atlantic: ". . . the sea there is swarming with fish which can be taken not only with the net but in baskets let down with a stone, so that it sinks in the water."

This was how the new land was unveiled, not with any special thunder of conquest but with a small note on its wildlife. Between the early 16th century and the mid-18th century, explorers, missionaries, trappers, fishermen, botanists and farmers were to find fishing grounds that yielded ten times the harvest of old world fisheries, seabird colonies containing millions of birds, unbroken forests of soft and hard woods covering more than one hundred thousand square miles, unimaginable populations of shellfish (with lobsters three and four feet long whose shells were cast up knee-deep on beaches after storms), skies darkened by flights of passenger pigeons, Eskimo curlews, sandpipers, flocks of geese and ducks numbering in the hundreds of thousands, and millions of seals pushing down from the Arctic as though proffered, one chronicler put it, "by the hand of God."

The new land was benign, but parts of it could also be incredibly hostile. When Jacques Cartier anchored at Blanc Sablon, after entering the Straits of Belle Isle in 1534, he wrote: "If the land was as good as the harbours there are, it would be an advantage; but it should not be named the New Land but a land of stones and rocks frightful and ill-shaped, for in all the said north coast I did not see a cartload of earth, though I landed in many places. Except at Blanc Sablon, there is nothing but moss and small stunted woods; in short, I deem rather than otherwise, that it is the land that God gave to Cain." Other travellers, a few of them, shared Cartier's perception of hard times ahead.

Gamaliel Smethurst, an English traveller of the 18th century, foresaw trouble. He wrote, in his *Narrative of an Extraordinary Escape out of the Hands of the Indians in the Gulf of St. Lawrence*: "But the Sea-cows, wild fowl, Indians, and beaver, will leave us as we settle in the country, and go to places less frequented." Smethurst saw only a small part of the 10,000 miles of shoreline of the region, and he scarcely suspected the size or wealth of the roughly 50,000 square miles of sea pastures, the shallow banks areas where fish teem, but his perception was acute. The region would not react well to the flood of men about to invade it.

The Atlantic region is more than the sum of its many parts. It provides a study of man's occupation of a primeval area, his destruction of much of it, his growing concern, and then his attempts to rebuild. Throughout this process, which in itself is a lesson in ecology—the study of living things and their relationships to each other and their environment—the natural history of the region is flung down all around the observer in a wealth of sight and sound.

THE ATLANTIC COAST:
AN ALBUM OF MAPS

The full colour maps on the following pages of this album were
especially commissioned for the series to illustrate the most
important aspects of the natural history of the Atlantic Coast region.

*The photograph on the next
two pages shows the area as seen
from a satellite high above the earth.*

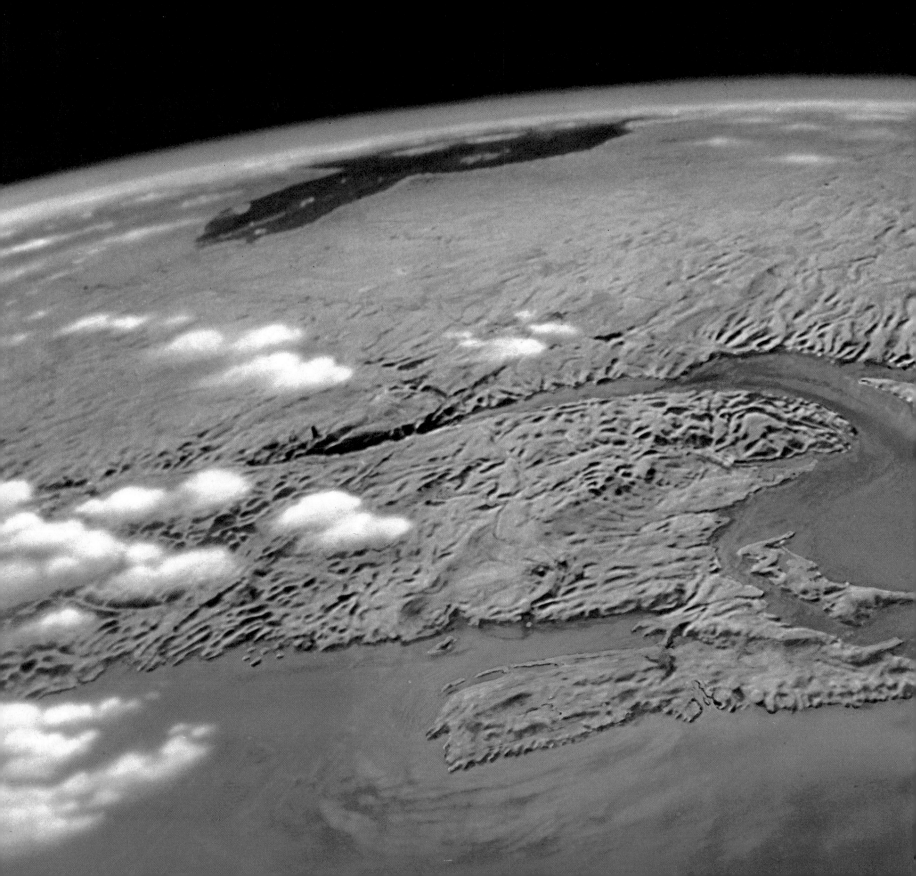

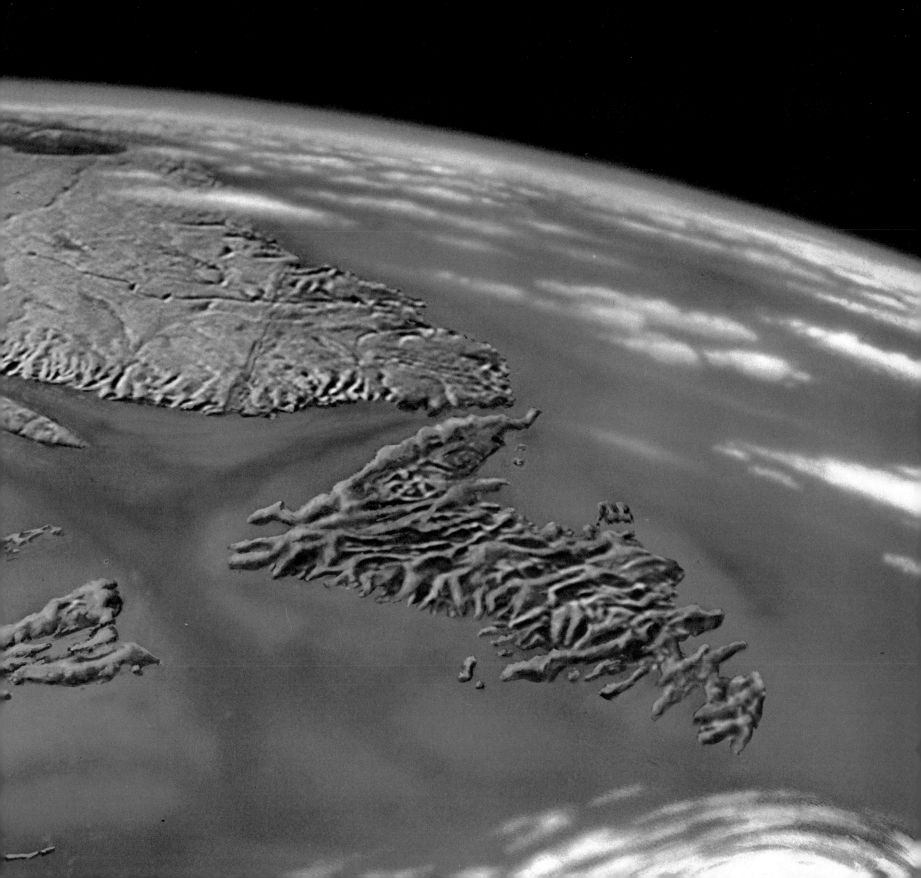

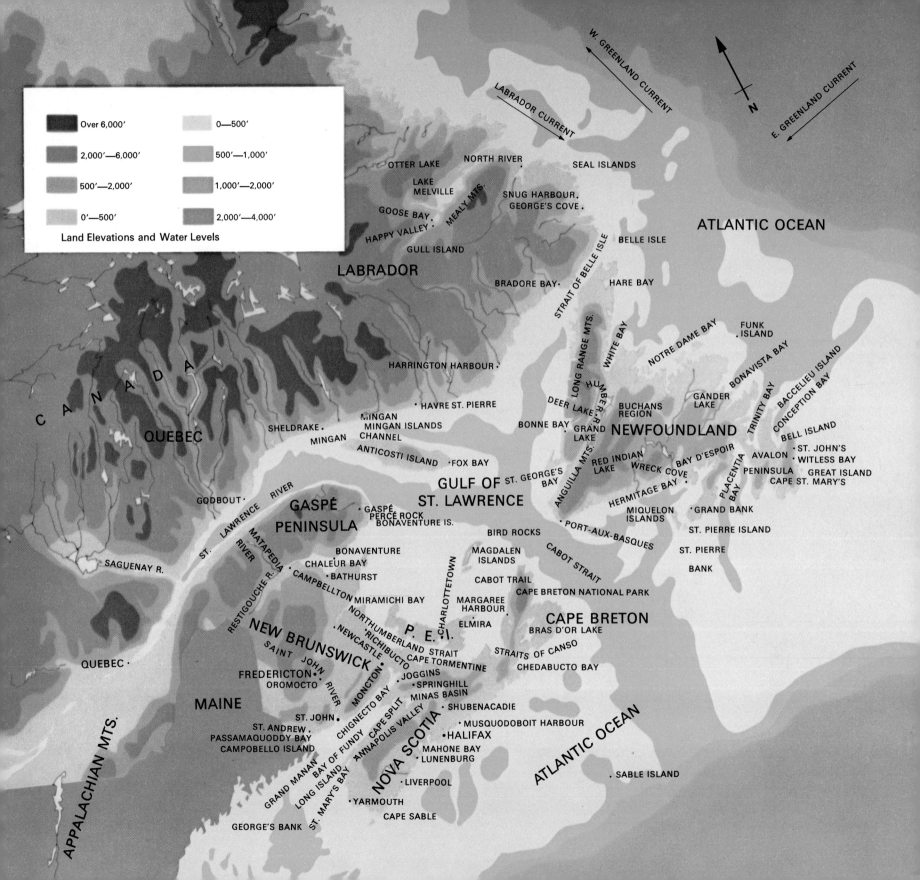

Land Elevations and Water Levels

Over 6,000′	0—500′
2,000′—6,000′	500′—1,000′
500′—2,000′	1,000′—2,000′
0′—500′	2,000′—4,000′

N

W. GREENLAND CURRENT

E. GREENLAND CURRENT

LABRADOR CURRENT

OTTER LAKE
NORTH RIVER
SEAL ISLANDS
LAKE MELVILLE
SNUG HARBOUR
GEORGE'S COVE
GOOSE BAY
MEALY MTS.
HAPPY VALLEY
GULL ISLAND

ATLANTIC OCEAN

LABRADOR

BELLE ISLE
BRADORE BAY
HARE BAY

FUNK ISLAND
WHITE BAY
NOTRE DAME BAY
BONAVISTA BAY
BACCELIEU ISLAND
CONCEPTION BAY
BELL ISLAND
GANDER LAKE
TRINITY BAY

HARRINGTON HARBOUR

LONG RANGE MTS.
HUMBER R.
DEER LAKE
BUCHANS REGION
BONNE BAY
GRAND LAKE
NEWFOUNDLAND

HAVRE ST. PIERRE

CANADA

QUEBEC

MINGAN
MINGAN ISLANDS
SHELDRAKE
MINGAN CHANNEL
ANTICOSTI ISLAND
FOX BAY

ANGUILLA MTS.
RED INDIAN LAKE
WRECK COVE
HERMITAGE BAY
BAY D'ESPOIR
ST. JOHN'S
WITLESS BAY
AVALON
PENINSULA
GREAT ISLAND
CAPE ST. MARY'S
PLACENTIA BAY

GODBOUT
GASPÉ PENINSULA
GASPÉ
PERCÉ ROCK
BONAVENTURE IS.

GULF OF
ST. LAWRENCE
ST. GEORGE'S BAY

PORT-AUX-BASQUES
MIQUELON ISLANDS
GRAND BANK
ST. PIERRE ISLAND
ST. PIERRE BANK

SAGUENAY R.
ST. LAWRENCE RIVER
ST. LAWRENCE RIVER
MATAPEDIA RIVER

BIRD ROCKS
MAGDALEN ISLANDS
CABOT STRAIT

BONAVENTURE
CHALEUR BAY
BATHURST
RESTIGOUCHE R.
CAMPBELLTON
MIRAMICHI BAY

CHARLOTTETOWN
CABOT TRAIL
CAPE BRETON NATIONAL PARK
MARGAREE HARBOUR
ELMIRA

CAPE BRETON
BRAS D'OR LAKE

QUEBEC

NEW BRUNSWICK
SAINT JOHN RIVER
NORTHUMBERLAND STRAIT
RICHIBUCTO
NEWCASTLE
CAPE TORMENTINE

P. E. I.

STRAITS OF CANSO
CHEDABUCTO BAY

FREDERICTON
OROMOCTO
MAINE
ST. JOHN
ST. ANDREW
PASSAMAQUODDY BAY
CAMPOBELLO ISLAND

MONCTON
CHIGNECTO BAY
JOGGINS
SPRINGHILL
MINAS BASIN
SHUBENACADIE
MUSQUODOBOIT HARBOUR

CAPE SPLIT
ANNAPOLIS VALLEY
HALIFAX
MAHONE BAY
LUNENBURG

ATLANTIC OCEAN

SABLE ISLAND

APPALACHIAN MTS.

GRAND MANAN
LONG ISLAND
BAY OF FUNDY
ST. MARY'S BAY
NOVA SCOTIA
LIVERPOOL

GEORGE'S BANK
YARMOUTH
CAPE SABLE

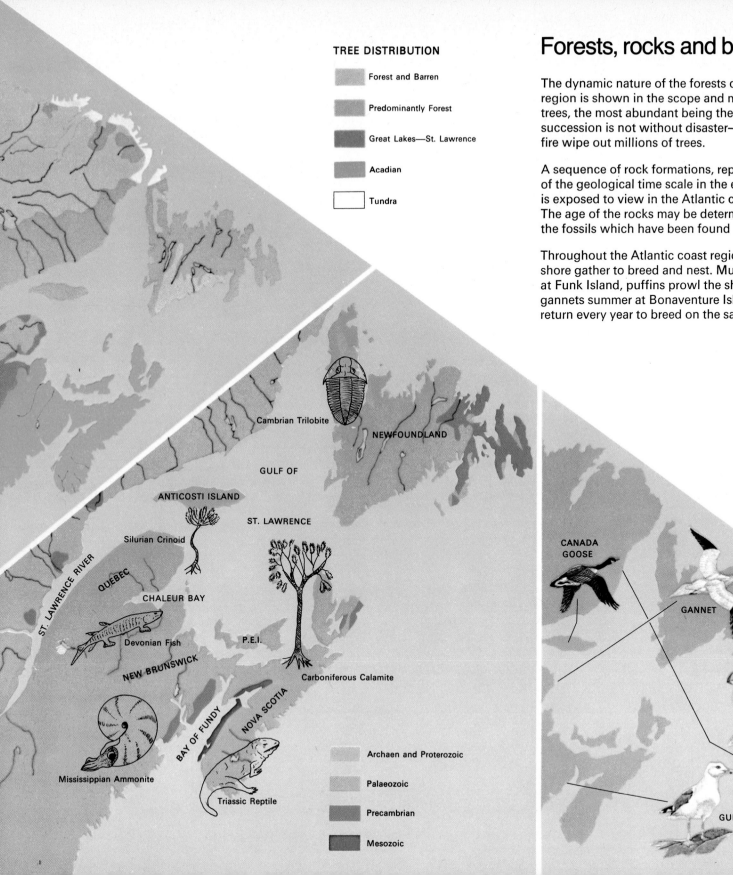

TREE DISTRIBUTION

- Forest and Barren
- Predominantly Forest
- Great Lakes—St. Lawrence
- Acadian
- Tundra

Cambrian Trilobite

NEWFOUNDLAND

GULF OF

ANTICOSTI ISLAND

ST. LAWRENCE

Silurian Crinoid

ST. LAWRENCE RIVER

QUEBEC

CHALEUR BAY

Devonian Fish

P.E.I.

NEW BRUNSWICK

Carboniferous Calamite

BAY OF FUNDY

NOVA SCOTIA

Mississippian Ammonite

Triassic Reptile

- Archaen and Proterozoic
- Palaeozoic
- Precambrian
- Mesozoic

Forests, rocks and birds

The dynamic nature of the forests of the Atlantic coast region is shown in the scope and mix of the varied trees, the most abundant being the balsam fir. Forest succession is not without disaster—gales, insects and fire wipe out millions of trees.

A sequence of rock formations, representative of most of the geological time scale in the earth's history, is exposed to view in the Atlantic coast region. The age of the rocks may be determined by studying the fossils which have been found in the rock layers.

Throughout the Atlantic coast region, birds of sea and shore gather to breed and nest. Murres mass together at Funk Island, puffins prowl the shorelines and the gannets summer at Bonaventure Island. Many seabirds return every year to breed on the same rocky ledges.

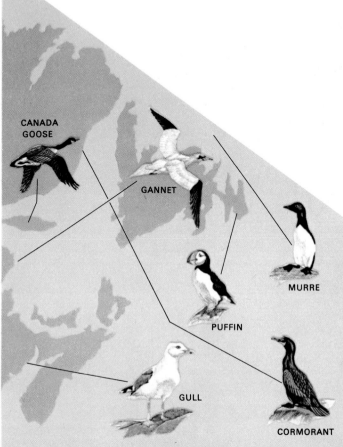

CANADA GOOSE

GANNET

MURRE

PUFFIN

GULL

CORMORANT

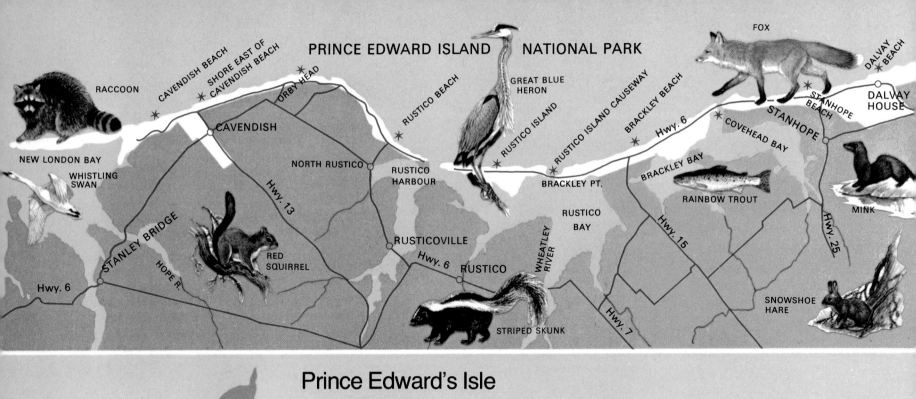

PRINCE EDWARD ISLAND NATIONAL PARK

RACCOON

CAVENDISH BEACH

SHORE EAST OF CAVENDISH BEACH

ORBY HEAD

CAVENDISH

NEW LONDON BAY

WHISTLING SWAN

NORTH RUSTICO

RUSTICO BEACH

GREAT BLUE HERON

RUSTICO ISLAND

RUSTICO ISLAND CAUSEWAY

BRACKLEY BEACH

Hwy. 6

FOX

STANHOPE BEACH

DALVAY BEACH

DALVAY HOUSE

STANHOPE

COVEHEAD BAY

RUSTICO HARBOUR

STANLEY BRIDGE

HOPE R.

Hwy. 13

RED SQUIRREL

RUSTICOVILLE

Hwy. 6

RUSTICO

WHEATLEY RIVER

RUSTICO BAY

BRACKLEY PT.

BRACKLEY BAY

RAINBOW TROUT

MINK

Hwy. 15

Hwy. 25

Hwy. 6

STRIPED SKUNK

Hwy. 7

SNOWSHOE HARE

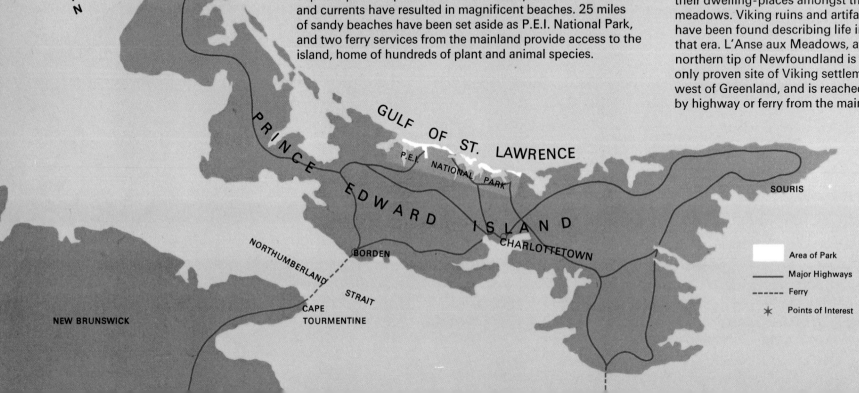

N

Prince Edward's Isle

Lying cradled in the curving shores of Nova Scotia and New Brunswick, Prince Edward Island was discovered by Jacques Cartier in 1534, and was described by him as "the fairest that may possibly be seen." Long before European man arrived the island was inhabited by the Micmac Indians. Sedimentary deposits picked up and moved forward by the action of waves and currents have resulted in magnificent beaches. 25 miles of sandy beaches have been set aside as P.E.I. National Park, and two ferry services from the mainland provide access to the island, home of hundreds of plant and animal species.

The New-found-land

About A.D. 1000 Leif Ericson and his Viking followers drew into the shores of eastern Canada and raised up their dwelling-places amongst the meadows. Viking ruins and artifacts have been found describing life in that era. L'Anse aux Meadows, at the northern tip of Newfoundland is the only proven site of Viking settlement west of Greenland, and is reached by highway or ferry from the mainland.

GULF OF ST. LAWRENCE

P.E.I. NATIONAL PARK

PRINCE EDWARD ISLAND

SOURIS

BORDEN

CHARLOTTETOWN

NORTHUMBERLAND STRAIT

NEW BRUNSWICK

CAPE TOURMENTINE

	Area of Park
	Major Highways
	Ferry
*	Points of Interest

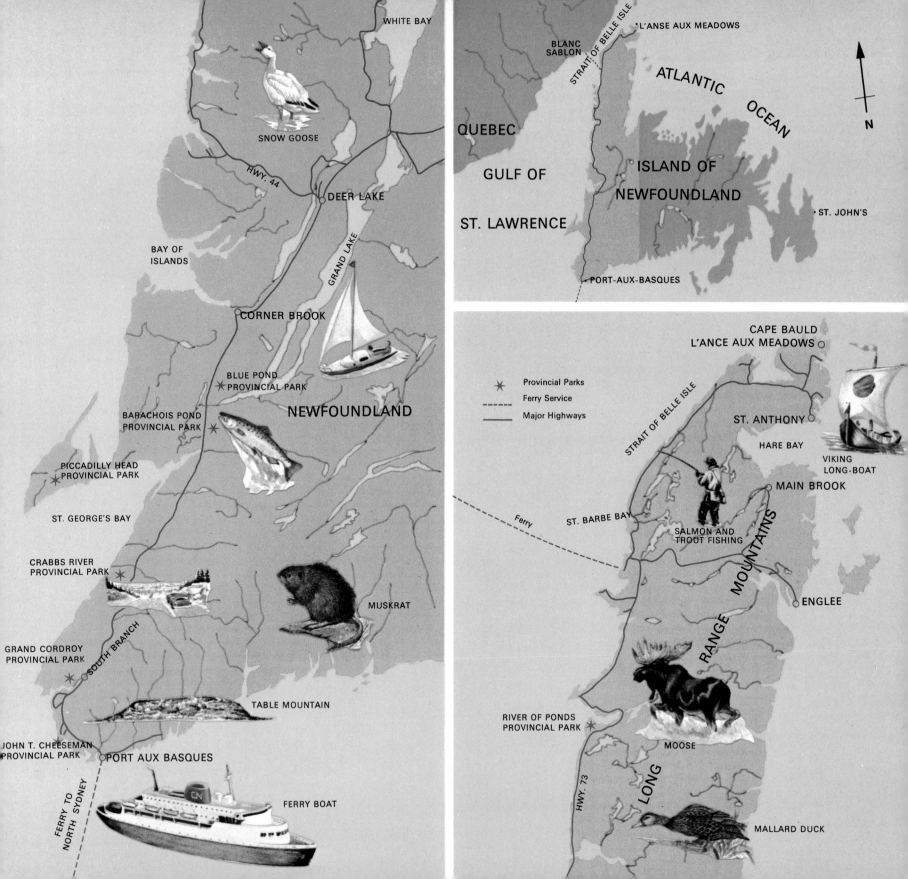

WHITE BAY

SNOW GOOSE

HWY. 44

DEER LAKE

BAY OF
ISLANDS

GRAND LAKE

CORNER BROOK

BLUE POND
PROVINCIAL PARK

BARACHOIS POND
PROVINCIAL PARK

NEWFOUNDLAND

PICCADILLY HEAD
PROVINCIAL PARK

ST. GEORGE'S BAY

CRABBS RIVER
PROVINCIAL PARK

MUSKRAT

GRAND CORDROY
PROVINCIAL PARK

SOUTH BRANCH

TABLE MOUNTAIN

JOHN T. CHEESEMAN
PROVINCIAL PARK

PORT AUX BASQUES

FERRY TO
NORTH SYDNEY

FERRY BOAT

BLANC
SABLON

L'ANSE AUX MEADOWS

STRAIT OF BELLE ISLE

ATLANTIC

QUEBEC

GULF OF

ISLAND OF

OCEAN

ST. LAWRENCE

NEWFOUNDLAND

· ST. JOHN'S

· PORT-AUX-BASQUES

N

CAPE BAULD
L'ANCE AUX MEADOWS ○

✱ Provincial Parks
- - - Ferry Service
—— Major Highways

ST. ANTHONY ○

HARE BAY

VIKING
LONG-BOAT

MAIN BROOK ○

STRAIT OF BELLE ISLE

ST. BARBE BAY

Ferry

SALMON AND
TROUT FISHING

RANGE MOUNTAINS

ENGLEE ○

RIVER OF PONDS
PROVINCIAL PARK ✱

MOOSE

HWY. 73

LONG

MALLARD DUCK

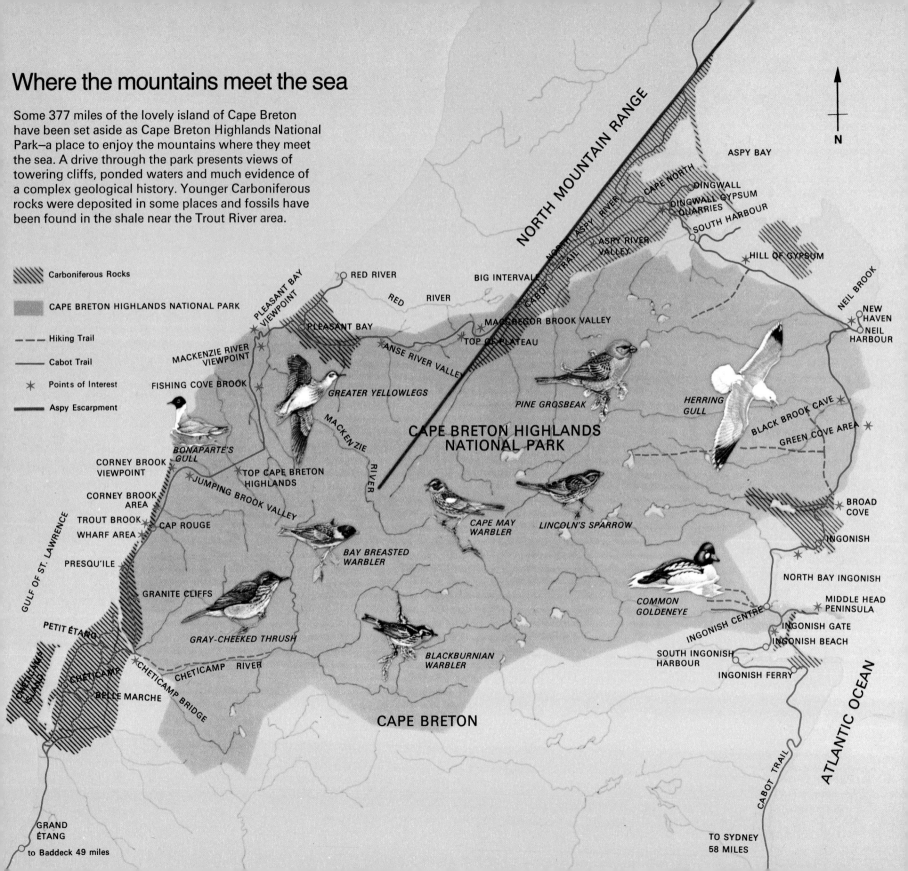

Where the mountains meet the sea

Some 377 miles of the lovely island of Cape Breton have been set aside as Cape Breton Highlands National Park—a place to enjoy the mountains where they meet the sea. A drive through the park presents views of towering cliffs, ponded waters and much evidence of a complex geological history. Younger Carboniferous rocks were deposited in some places and fossils have been found in the shale near the Trout River area.

Carboniferous Rocks

CAPE BRETON HIGHLANDS NATIONAL PARK

Hiking Trail

Cabot Trail

Points of Interest

Aspy Escarpment

NORTH MOUNTAIN RANGE

ASPY BAY

CAPE NORTH

DINGWALL

DINGWALL GYPSUM QUARRIES

SOUTH HARBOUR

HILL OF GYPSUM

NORTH ASPY RIVER

ASPY RIVER VALLEY

CABOT TRAIL

BIG INTERVAL

RED RIVER

RED RIVER

MACGREGOR BROOK VALLEY

NEIL BROOK

NEW HAVEN

NEIL HARBOUR

PLEASANT BAY VIEWPOINT

ANSE RIVER VALLEY

TOP OF PLATEAU

PLEASANT BAY

MACKENZIE RIVER VIEWPOINT

GREATER YELLOWLEGS

PINE GROSBEAK

HERRING GULL

BLACK BROOK CAVE

GREEN COVE AREA

FISHING COVE BROOK

MACKENZIE RIVER

CAPE BRETON HIGHLANDS NATIONAL PARK

BONAPARTE'S GULL

CORNEY BROOK VIEWPOINT

TOP CAPE BRETON HIGHLANDS

JUMPING BROOK VALLEY

CAPE MAY WARBLER

LINCOLN'S SPARROW

BROAD COVE

CORNEY BROOK AREA

TROUT BROOK

CAP ROUGE

INGONISH

WHARF AREA

PRESQU'ILE

BAY BREASTED WARBLER

NORTH BAY INGONISH

GRANITE CLIFFS

COMMON GOLDENEYE

MIDDLE HEAD PENINSULA

INGONISH GATE

GRAY-CHEEKED THRUSH

INGONISH CENTRE

INGONISH BEACH

PETIT ÉTANG

SOUTH INGONISH HARBOUR

BLACKBURNIAN WARBLER

CHETICAMP

CHETICAMP RIVER

CHETICAMP BRIDGE

BELLE MARCHE

INGONISH FERRY

GULF OF ST. LAWRENCE

CHETICAMP ISLAND

CAPE BRETON

ATLANTIC OCEAN

GRAND ÉTANG

to Baddeck 49 miles

TO SYDNEY 58 MILES

CABOT TRAIL

PART ONE / THE REGION

1 GRAND BANKS TO FUNDY

The region of the Atlantic shore, or the Maritimes, as it is called, is precisely confined by natural boundaries. On the east is the fence of the Labrador Current which flows down the east coast of Newfoundland, and along the south is the barrier of the Gulf Stream. The Quebec shoreline is the northern limit, and the western division is the mainland mass of the Appalachian geographical system which begins in Alabama and sweeps up the eastern coast of America through Newfoundland.

For historical and biological reasons, the Grand Banks can be viewed as a kind of fulcrum on which almost all other human life of the region has hinged since the earliest days. The fertile banks, southeast of Newfoundland, are warmed by the sun, fed by the cool, plankton-laden Labrador Current from the north, and caressed by the warm, life-laden Gulf Stream from the southwest. They are almost the same size and shape as the island of Newfoundland, with an average depth of only about two hundred feet, a kind of sunken sister island. The banks are immensely fertile, they provide excellent habitats for bottom-feeding creatures, and the interaction of the warm and cold currents creates ideal conditions for plankton production. The result is immense populations of cod, haddock, rosefish, pollack, herring and mackerel which are pursued by fleets of draggers, schooners, and trawlers from North America and Europe.

The fertility of the banks, some geologists have noted, is the lost fertility of Newfoundland. The last glacial age, according to one theory, scraped off Newfoundland's soil and dumped it offshore to create the banks. It is more likely, however, that the banks are just an expansion of the continental shelf which runs down the coast of North America. The important thing about the banks is their average thirty-fathom depth, ideal for vast herds of grazing fish and the bottom dwellers they feed on.

Newfoundland, so close, shrouded in the same mist that often covers the banks, is nowhere near as productive of animal life as the chill waters of the banks. When John Cabot landed there, it was an island of forests, and basically, it still is. He found mostly softwoods; spruce, both black and white, balsam fir, and some fairly extensive stands of white pine which have gone today. The early settlers were dependent on wood for survival, and nearly all the settled coasts of Newfoundland are now bare of trees. The coastal villages, or outports, stand on ground as bare and as empty as a moonscape. In places, the settlers burned so frequently in their attempt to get cleared agricultural land that they created barren lands now totally and probably permanently treeless which can only support stunted scrub, grazing animals like caribou, ground birds like willow ptarmigans, and meagre populations of songbirds.

The Avalon peninsula, the southeastern portion of the island, is the centre of human occupation. It consists of a low plateau about 700 feet above sea level which covers 4,000 square miles and includes 1,400 square miles of tundra-like barrens. The soils are shallow and acid and are not too suitable for tree growth. The frequent gales and sleet storms which locals call the glitters, along with an annual snowfall of about one hundred inches, make it a bleak prospect for any form of life not distinctly adapted to it. Into this area is packed more than half of Newfoundland's population of about half a million people, a small population of caribou, some moose, a few snowshoe hares, and a large number of willow ptarmigans.

The first view of Newfoundland may seem forbidding; many observers speak of the silence, the waiting atmosphere, and yet it possesses a special quality unique in the Maritimes. It is akin, perhaps, to that of the Arctic. From a hilltop, or from a low-flying plane, the land seems purple, hushed, brooding, with thick forests marching around pallid silver lakes. Mist lies in the hollows and skies are grey with the suggestion of moving clouds.

When William Cormack began his east-to-west trek across the island, he took a walk through half a dozen geological ages. In the eastern, or Atlantic, uplands, he was in very ancient country, the rocks under his feet laid down four or five hundred million years ago, in the Cambrian period, more than one hundred million years before plants colonized the land. As he trudged on, he crossed river after river, all plunging south to the tall cliffs of the island's south shore, most of them emplaced more recently, during the Devonian period of about 300 million years ago. He watched carefully for animals, was disappointed to see so few of them in many places. But in the lakes that he passed, and rivers that he crossed, were the island's greatest animal resource, fish. In the northern regions of this upland country were streams which might contain five or six thousand migrant salmon during spawning runs. He was in the land of the ouananiche, the landlocked salmon, and of the landlocked char and smelt. After walking one hundred miles, he reached the Hermitage Bay region where he moved into a country of sedimentary rocks, limestones, dolomites, shales, argillites and sandstones, four-hundred-million-year-old Ordovician territory.

He walked through what we now call the boreal forest region which comprises most of the forest land of all the rest of Canada, stretching as a continuous belt of timber from Newfoundland and Labrador to the Rocky Mountains, and thence into Alaska. He watched migrant geese and ducks gathering on lakes and streams in readiness for fall migration, saw the tracks made by large herds of caribou in their north-south migrations across the island. Constantly, he looked for signs of the legendary Newfoundland Indians, the Beothucks, but by that time, they were very close to extinction under the guns of white men and rival Micmac Indians from the mainland.

He pushed on across great expanses of Devonian and Ordovician country that dominates south-central Newfoundland toward the western highlands which run like a double spine up the Gulf of St. Lawrence side of the island—the Long Range Mountains in the north, the Serpentine Range in the south, the Topsail Hills southeast of Grand Lake, the Dunamagon Highlands between White Bay and Notre Dame Bay, and finally, the Anguille Mountains east of the Long Range.

At last, after nearly dying in an early winter blizzard, Cormack reached the west coast of the island and the shores of the Gulf of St. Lawrence.

The gulf is almost an inland sea, a semi-contained area of 57,000 square miles with only two outlets to the ocean, the Cabot Strait which separates Newfoundland and Cape Breton, and the Strait of Belle Isle between Newfoundland and Labrador. It is fed by inflow through Belle Isle and down the St. Lawrence River which is the drain channel for 500,000 square miles of hinterland stretching west to Lake Superior. Cutting across the seabed of the gulf is the Laurentian Channel, up to 250 fathoms deep, which cuts from the edge of the continental shelf to near the Saguenay River, and is a monument to the massive movement of ice in other geological ages. The gulf is also notable, biologically speaking, for the Magdalen Shallows. These sprawl over most of the southwestern area, and their shallow depths, together with their protection from the force of south and west winds by the New Brunswick and Nova Scotia coastlines, makes them warm in summer and a host to oyster legions and other creatures.

The northern fringe of the gulf is the low, undistinguished, rocky coast of the south shore of Quebec, perhaps the most ill-served of all the Maritime regions from a natural history point of view. It lacks a really abundant inshore cod fishery. It does not have any important, life-giving currents, many of its rocks are Ordovician, and most of its soil was scraped off by the last glaciation which left the region strewn with boulders. Finally, its shoreline is unserved by either road or rail, and its people, isolated in small fishing villages, live close to the earth. For centuries, they have moved to the rocky shore, or to equally rocky offshore islands, during the fleeting summers to seize a crop of codfish or a harvest of seabird eggs or, in the early spring, a killing of migrating seals. In the winters, they retreat inland for shelter and hunt caribou.

The gulf shore, still in Quebec, continues on the other side of the mouth of the St. Lawrence, at Gaspé Peninsula. Here, the quality of life changes measurably. The geology has, in places, created a kinder environment. There is still much old rock, Ordovician, but it is mixed with the more recent Devonian, the most visible and undisturbed lower Devonian sections to a geologist in the Appalachian system, in fact. The soil is still poor but here and there it is good enough to farm. There are roads and good fishing grounds and the coast often has a stark beauty that is missing from the south shore of Quebec.

Inland, the central highlands extend from the southwest to the northeast, consisting of ninety percent sedimentary rocks some of which are locally metamorphosed, and having a high point at 4,160 feet in the McGerrigle Mountains (formerly Tabletop). Uplands in the northwest consist of folded sedimentary rocks. In the east, lowlands lie over Carboniferous sandstone, the geological period that created the world's coal.

The coastline is punctuated by a great natural phenomenon, the deep cut Chaleur Bay (a drowned valley) which once hosted enormous assemblages of sturgeon, herring, lobsters, oysters, seabirds, mackerel, whales, seals, walrus and salmon. Most of the primeval populations have gone, or have been cut down drastically, but salmon still abound along the coast.

All the river valleys of New Brunswick run mainly from southwest to the northeast, thus following the general physiographic trend of the province and of the Appalachian system generally. In early times, nearly all held salmon and other anadromous fish, especially the Miramichi, just south of Chaleur Bay, which was, before Caucasian man, the greatest salmon-spawning river on earth.

The early settlers of Nova Scotia, looking at its sweeping forests, tumbling streams, its many lakes and ponds, had high hopes of creating a garden paradise. But the geology is heavily Ordovician over eighty per cent of the peninsula. Many early settlements went bankrupt finding out that the soil grows trees and not much else. In fact, only about five per cent of the 21,400 square miles of the province is any good for agriculture. The settlers burned and chopped and ploughed anyway, the British cleaned out all the large white pines for the Royal Navy, and reduced large areas to stunted scrub and barrenland. Only in the central peninsula, in the Annapolis Valley, in the Cumberland Basin, and in other odd lowland areas did the soil respond to the plough and the planter.

Lastly, there is the incredible Bay of Fundy: it is less a bay than a huge, flooded valley two hundred miles long, covering six thousand square miles of quite shallow sea, around 275 feet deep. It is a funnel into which is compressed the water thrust forward by tidal action. This produces tides which rise about ten feet at the mouth of the bay but are fifty feet or more deeper inside the bay.

The daily influx and outflow of the tides create unique and interesting environments through much of the Fundy area, particularly the tidal marshlands at the head of the bay. These marshlands once covered thousands of acres, before the Acadian French began dyking and draining in the early 17th century, a task that has been finished in the 20th century. Great marsh meadows now produce hay. The Minas Basin which digs into Nova Scotia's neck is a tidal area where the tide withdraws almost out of sight in places. In summer, the exposed sand and mud absorb heat and when the chill tide comes in (there is no Gulf Stream water here) the water is warmed during its passage over the tidal lands and local residents can swim in the sea.

The turbulence of the Bay of Fundy is increased by the inflow of three big rivers which modify its circulation and its production of marine life. The Petitcodiac, at the head of the bay, is notable for its twice-a-day tidal bore. The St. John River, the biggest of the three and navigable for eighty-eight miles, is rudely thrust back twice a day by the Fundy tide, causing the famous "reversing falls" in the city of Saint John when the river seems to double back on itself. Lastly, the St. Croix River debouches into Passamaquoddy Bay at the southwest end of Fundy. Passamaquoddy, because of a peculiar system of tides and currents, is the production ground for the world's greatest populations of herring.

The Atlantic shore of Canada is by ecological observation and measurement, a diverse, contradictory and fascinating region. It is both a series of sharply contrasting environments and a single environment, made an entity by the omnipresent sea.

The funnelling effect of the Bay of Fundy compresses the tides, reaching up to fifty feet inside the bay, while only ten feet at the mouth.

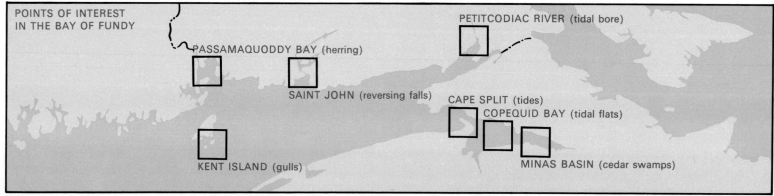

POINTS OF INTEREST
IN THE BAY OF FUNDY

PASSAMAQUODDY BAY (herring)

PETITCODIAC RIVER (tidal bore)

SAINT JOHN (reversing falls)

CAPE SPLIT (tides)

COPEQUID BAY (tidal flats)

KENT ISLAND (gulls)

MINAS BASIN (cedar swamps)

2 A FRIEZE OF ISLANDS

The Atlantic region is studded with islands—Anticosti, the Magdalens, the French islands of St. Pierre and Miquelon, Cape Breton, Prince Edward, Sable, Grand Manan, and thousands of others, some large enough to contain one farm, some small enough to be overcrowded by two gulls' nests. It is islands that first catch the attention of the traveller, the biologist, the geographer and the mariner, and it is islands which give the region much of its unique atmosphere. Islands give refuge to seabirds and shelter to fishermen in storms. They create odd, individualistic populations of animals and men.

St. Pierre and Miquelon, huddled against Newfoundland's south shore, are nothing much more than chunks of granite and sand which give the French a jump-off point for the fishing of the Grand Banks. The Magdalens, a sixty-mile-long string of roughly-connected dunes, sand bars, lagoons, broken into fifteen islands set a little off-centre in the Gulf of St. Lawrence, are an enclave of the most isolated, French-English-stock fishermen in the Atlantic region. More than 10,000 people live on fewer than 50,000 acres of the island group, making the Magdalens one of the most densely populated rural areas in the world, a testimony to the fertility of the sea around their unproductive shores.

Geologists cannot decide to what extent the Magdalen group was glaciated, but there are some glacial deposits. A ridge of moraine shows on Coffin Island, consisting largely of granite, banded gneiss and amphibolite, immensely old and typical rocks of the Labrador peninsula. The rock formations of the islands are both sedimentary and igneous and were laid down in the coal-forest Carboniferous, around 280 million years ago, but the younger geology does not host fertile soils as it may elsewhere.

Anticosti Island, as large as the other major island in the gulf, Prince Edward, resembles it only in size. Its low hills, never more than five hundred feet above sea level, are heavily wooded with black spruce, white birch interspersed with red maple and mountain ash, and run most of the length of the island. Its hundreds of small ponds and lakes, its boglands, its thick black spruce growth on the flatlands once echoed to the sound of French guns as a French chocolate millionaire, who owned the island outright, took his guests hunting. His imported moose, elk, wapiti wandered among the wild roses, red-berried elders, wild grasses and herbs which abound at the well-drained western end of the island. Today, it is owned by a lumber company, but the hand of man, despite the logging, seems hardly to have touched the island's raw, primitive beauty.

Each island shares a function of natural history, but each is unique in some way. At the head of the Gaspé is Percé Rock, a long sliver of stone shaped exactly like an aircraft carrier, with its bow pointed toward the mainland and its flat top packed with nesting cormorants and gulls in summer. Nearby Bonaventure, wooded, and a refuge for fewer than a dozen people, hosts one of the world's great gannet colonies along its towering eastern cliffs.

Jacques Cartier was the first chronicler of Prince Edward Island which hugs the southern shore of the gulf. He sailed along the northwest coast of the island and saw what he called cedars, yews, pines, white elms, ashes, willows, peas, gooseberries, strawberries, raspberries, pigeons and ring doves. The island, in those days, was almost completely forested, although there were some parkland-like areas. It is 110 miles long and is nowhere higher than 500 feet above sea level, nor wider than thirty miles. The western end of the island is low-lying, the home of cedar and tamarack swamps. Cartier's description makes the island sound like an abundant wild garden, a reputation that has survived the intervening four hundred years. Today, its patchwork fields of strawberries, potatoes and hay, its neat clumps of woodlots, its startling red soil, and its sweeping white beaches make Prince Edward Island the most bountifully-endowed of all the maritime geographic regions.

It is actually an extension of a lowland area on 250-million-year-old rocks that thrust into New Brunswick and Nova Scotia. All of the island's shallow valleys march on out into the sea, and this indicates that, at one time, the island either sank or was flooded. It is surrounded by shallows, a confirmation, perhaps, of the flooding theory. These shallows create ideal conditions for unique marine life. The action of the water in these shallows and the erosion of the coasts of Prince Edward Island have piled up great masses of sand into bars, spits and beaches, the last-named a great feature of the island. This sand comes from the dredging

of offshore waves, the erosion of bedrock in the sea, and the movement of the glacial deposits which cover the island in some places. Essentially, the island is composed of glacial droppings which, unlike Newfoundland, are composed of deep soils. Some of this soil appears to have been scraped from New Brunswick and the highland country in New Brunswick and Quebec. At another point in the glaciation, it seems to have come from the nearer highlands of Cape Breton. Whatever the origin, most of the soil consists of sandy red clays. The soil is stained its bright red by the iron oxide present in the original bedrock. Underneath the red soil are red beds of rock, sandstone, siltstone and some shale.

Prince Edward Island's sandy beaches are magnificent and rare in the Maritimes because of the generally rocky shorelines. They are formed of almost pure quartz sand, a hard white mineral with a glassy appearance. Compared with other rocks, the quartz is "tough," and resistant to being broken down chemically, but these wave-swept beaches may be the graveyard of a chain of mountains long since worn down by the ceaseless action of wind, rain and sea.

It is, therefore, something of a surprise to move only forty miles east to another island and to find it of a totally different character. Cape Breton is separated from the Nova Scotia mainland by the narrow Strait of Canso. The loss of its soil through moving ice left Cape Breton with an austere but beautiful topography. Geologically, it consists of an uptilted and eroded surface of Cretaceous peneplains which sink into the Atlantic on the east, with many drowned valleys, and rise, like wedges, to the north and west, to the high sea cliffs. There are traces of a low coastal plain, seen in the land that slopes gently toward the sea and terminates in long, curving beaches. It is highland country, at least along its western shores, and it drew highland settlers. Its soaring, rocky cliffs, up to 1800 feet, are laced along the western shore by the Cabot Trail, a spectacular scenic highway that commemorates the fact that this was the first landfall of the Cabots in 1497. It is poor country, however, for settlement, and only the rich deposits of coal in the northeast section redeem it economically.

◄ *The stained sands of beautiful Cavendish Beach, Prince Edward Island, evidence the presence of red iron oxide in the area's original bedrock.*

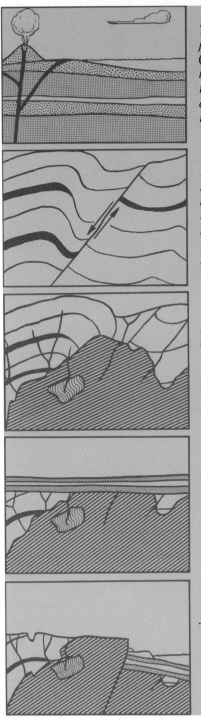

The earliest event recorded is a period of deposition of sedimentary (dotted area) and volcanic (heavy lines) rocks in distant Precambrian time, more than 750 million years ago. Processes of sedimentation are the same now as they were then.

Ancient sedimentary and volcanic rocks were folded, broken by faults, and over a long period became changed in their mineral makeup by the increased pressure and temperature which came as a result of the folding and faulting.

The already altered rocks were intruded by masses of granite (shaded) with numerous offshoots called "dykes" (heavy lines). Blocks of the ancient rock drifted into the granite and were partly ingested (wavy lines).

Erosion smoothed away the whole complex of ancient rocks with the granite intrusions and dykes. Additional sedimentary rocks were laid down on top of this surface during the Carboniferous period, about 280 million years ago.

Uplift and erosion followed some faulting. In places Carboniferous rocks were stripped off; a veneer of rubble was left by glaciation. Erosion may best be seen at the coasts (right edge) and in stream valleys (nick at top).

The Bras D'Or, a scenically-beautiful salt lake with a multitude of bays and inlets, occupies nearly a quarter of the centre of Cape Breton Island.

Nearly one-quarter of the centre of the island consists of a salt lake, the Bras d'Or, a miniature inland sea which, with its multitude of arms, inlets and bays set against a background of wildflower-strewn slopes and blue mountains, gives it some of the most spectacular scenery in the Maritimes.

There is one last important island in the Maritime region. Although it is insignificant in terms of size, economy or beauty, it has exerted a sombre influence on the rest of the region. This is Sable Island, a crescent-shaped sliver of sand standing alone more than one hundred miles off the coast of Nova Scotia. On its shores, and on the sand bars that surround it, about five thousand fishermen, sailors, soldiers and merchantmen have died in shipwrecks since the 16th century. It is barely a mile wide at its widest point, and about sixteen miles long. Like Cape Breton, it has a lake, Lake Wallace. About fifty per cent of its mass is more or less stabilized by grass, but the island itself is only a small part of the sand bar system that surrounds it. To the west are roughly twenty miles of sand bars, called the West Bar, over which breakers crash almost continuously. To the east is another bar, the East Bar, which is not quite as turbulent as the West Bar, although it has claimed almost as many ships. The entire island is surrounded by sand bars, from six to twelve feet under the surface of the water, and they change position with every storm.

The moving sands have, through the ages, disturbed visitors as they meander along exploring the narrow shoreline during a trip to the island. A casual walk along the great ocean beach of the eastern fringe of the island occasionally reveals skulls, jawbones, ribs and other human bones, along with the remains of Elizabethan pistols or walrus tusks, rising like ghosts up from the endlessly moving sands.

3 THE WINDS AND THE WEATHER

A 19th century resident of Sable Island, S. D. McDonald, got out of bed one morning, looked out of his bedroom window, and saw a clear bright sun rising. As he dressed, however, his room went dark. A dull haze had suddenly covered the sun. The sky, as McDonald was to note later, "assumed a wild, unusual appearance." The wind became a gale and whipped off the tops of waves and sand dunes alike. The morning became as dark as night. McDonald shouted but the storm drowned his voice. Lightning fled up and down the roaring beaches. Then, McDonald said, "gradually the storm ceases, the clouds break and pack away in dense black masses to leeward and the sea alone retains its wild tumult."

When visitors to the Maritimes complain about the weather, locals have a standard reply: "Wait a minute. It'll change." No weather year is like any other. A Maritime summer may be a series of perfect, sunny warm days. Or it may be weeks of fogs, gales and rain. The speed of its change is the chief characteristic of Maritime weather. Squalls, boiling up in seconds, have killed hundreds of fishermen. Sharp changes between day and night temperatures mean that shore residents may sunburn as though they lived in Florida but huddle over log fires at night in midsummer, in order to keep warm.

The weather of the Atlantic region is diverse, variable and relatively mild because of the leavening effect of the sea. Cyclonic storms control the weather throughout the region. They pass along the southern reaches in winter and induce invasions of cold air from the interior. In summer, they pass to the north and draw in warm air from the south and southwest.

Summer air movements, usually continental in origin, come into the gulf region from the west and northwest and are modified as they move over the coastal areas. In winter, however, the air tends to run west. The oceanic winds are warm and wet so that almost everywhere temperatures are up to ten degrees higher than, say, in Quebec City.

The western North Atlantic distribution of atmospheric pressure points dominates Maritime climate. This distribution has two sponsors, the Icelandic Low, a low pressure area between Greenland and Iceland with anti-clockwise winds, and the Bermuda-Azores High with great clockwise winds over much of the North Atlantic. The Icelandic Low is most active and expansive in winter; the Bermuda-Azores High may expand up to five hundred miles north during the summer months.

From these two systems spring all Maritime weather. The Icelandic Low brings strong westerlies in the middle latitudes in winter. The Bermuda-Azores High brings summer westerlies. From the south come violent interruptions in this conventional circulation–hurricanes. Sometimes they are deflected up the coast of North America and reach the Maritimes as severe gales. McDonald's Sable Island gale was just such a deflection.

Changes in the force and direction of winds alter currents and, ultimately, the disposition of oceanic life. When the Bermuda-Azores High is intensified, the Gulf Stream tends to increase its rate of flow. When the high pressure system migrates north, the Gulf Stream moves closer to the Maritimes. A more intense Icelandic Low, on the other hand, boosts the force of the southward-flowing Labrador Current. This creates increased circulation within the seas, makes deeper waters well up, and causes countless overturns and displacements of marine life.

Weather in the Maritimes is, therefore, the product of climatic forces that are both oceanic and continental. Newfoundland is an island but its climate has much of the savagery of the mainland's. The island's air movements swing in mainly from the west. If it were not for the ameliorating influence of the Labrador Current and the Gulf Stream, the climate likely would be pure continental. As it is, while the cool sea helps modify extreme winter cold, it delays the peak of summer warmth until August. It creates great fogs along the east coast because of the interaction of offshore currents and air masses. Some of these fogs are so dense that a fishing boat passing into one of them looks as though it were being driven into a solid wall.

Newfoundland gets an annual snowfall of ten feet as does Prince Edward Island where it also rains every third day. Prince Edward Island has a boisterous, late spring but its slow-waning fall is probably the best time of the year on the island.

New Brunswick has a near-to-continental climate in the north, as does Quebec's Gaspé, and winter temperatures in the uplands commonly drop to forty below. Summer temperatures close to one hundred degrees are fairly common. Southern New

Brunswick is more uniform, closer to the "oceanic" climates of Newfoundland and Prince Edward Island, which do not suffer from such continental extremes as the northern part of the province does.

Nova Scotia possesses both the continental and oceanic climates, although not with the same force as Newfoundland. It is a wet region, cloudy sixty per cent of the time, with an annual average temperature of forty-five degrees.

In this century, the Bermuda-Azores High is intensifying and increasing the flow of warmer waters from the Gulf Stream. Nobody knows what governs its strength, nor why it wanders as much as five hundred miles a year. Clearly, it is part of complex planetary flows of air and movements of pressure which themselves may be related to sunspots or slight changes in sea temperatures.

The Icelandic Low seems to be weakening, cutting down the counter-clockwise wind stress in the eastern North Atlantic. As a result, the ocean is getting warmer and the climate of the Maritimes is gradually changing. This may, of course, be merely a cyclical trend. Apparently, there was a warm period from 1870 to 1890, and a cool period in the first twenty years of this century. The Halifax air temperature, for instance, which averaged 43 degrees in 1875, went up to nearly 45 in 1900. It was down again to about 43.5 in 1920 when it began another steady rise that continued until 1950 when it started to fall again. Temperatures taken in 1922 at St. Andrew's wharf in New Brunswick show that there was an average water temperature of 45 degrees throughout the year. By 1933, this was up to 46, and in 1950 it was 48. By 1955, the temperature was dropping again, down to less than 47.

Cyclical or not, for all life the temperature of air and water is vital. The fate of a species may depend on temperature stability to within five degrees. There is evidence to suggest that the early Norse settlement which was established in 986 on the coast of Greenland depended on the inshore cod fishery to supplement the meagre farming. But in the 14th century, some oceanographers theorize, the waters around Greenland warmed. This drove the Greenland codfish stocks farther north, perhaps off the shore altogether. The Norsemen, already precariously clinging to the land, were likely wiped out by a combination of starvation, disease, and Europe's gradual disinterest in them

as they became unable either to export or import.

Many animals are similarly delicately balanced. One of the caribou's greatest enemies is the spring plague of bot and nose flies which, at its worst, can break up caribou herds. For the caribou, survival depends on getting their calves born and independent well before the crisis dates–around June 8 to June 12–when the main bodies of flies begin to emerge. Any calf born after June 6 stands a poor chance of survival. A two-degree increase in Maritime temperature could leave the caribou defenseless against the earlier-appearing flies.

But the present warming spell creates opportunities for new forms of life. Within the last ten years, sailfish have begun to penetrate the Bay of Fundy from George's Banks off the coast of Massachusetts. Since 1936, mackerel have been forcing their way up the east coast of Newfoundland in large numbers. Also in 1936, fourteen gannets–since grown to a colony of several thousand–established themselves on Funk Island. Their colonizing perhaps was related to the young mackerel in the area. At the beginning of this century, the Greenland codfish stocks were tiny, limited to a relatively few fish that migrated up and down the coast, probably in pursuit of capelin or launce food stocks. Today, Greenland cod stocks are gigantic.

The extent to which atmospheric changes influence the waters is global, and climate in the Maritimes may, in fact, depend on events thousands of miles away. When Nansen took the Fram Expedition into the Arctic in the mid-1890's, he found a surface layer of polar water 650 feet thick, with temperatures down to three degrees Fahrenheit. But beneath that was warmer water of Atlantic origin with temperatures nearly two degrees centigrade above zero. Subsequently, Russian polar expeditions showed that the surface layer of polar water had thinned to between 200 and 400 feet thick. The Atlantic water underneath had warmed up to almost five degrees above zero. In this century, the Gulf Stream has warmed by 3.6 degrees which has appreciably changed the climates of Greenland, Iceland, Scandinavia and, less dramatically, the Maritimes.

Because they are so close to the Gulf Stream and the Labrador Current and come under the leavening influence of westerlies, the Maritimes can be likened to a warm haven sitting under a cap of ice. The polar ice cap smothers nearly two million square miles of sea, and from this cap, which is always expanding, comes an almost constant flood of ice. Some of it reaches the Maritimes.

The ice is broken away from the Arctic at thousands of points and is carried along by the east and west Greenland Currents, and the Baffin Land Current. The ice threads among islands of the Canadian archipelago, through Hudson Strait and into the Labrador Current. It is hundreds of square miles of pack and floe ice on which animals, especially seals, ride south. It includes as many as 50,000 icebergs, the largest of which may reach into transatlantic shipping lanes and endanger shipping. The icebergs break off, or, rather, are calved, from Greenland glaciers and are spilled into countless glass-smooth inlets surrounded by towering, snow-capped hills. A single iceberg may be a mile long and weigh many millions of tons.

As it floats out from Jakobshavn Glacier into Davis Strait, for instance, chunks of it begin to splinter and break away, and from then on, the life cycle of the iceberg is a continual process of breaking, melting, overturning and moving south. By the time the berg gets into the grip of the Labrador Current, it is rolling steadily from side to side as it goes through its cycle of overturns. By the time it reaches Newfoundland, months after being calved, sixty per cent of its bulk is gone. Its eventual death, which will be rapid once it gets within reach of the Gulf Stream, may occur three years after leaving Jakobshavn.

The flow of ice is actually triple-pronged since some of it branches away from the Labrador Current and goes through the Straits of Belle Isle to join other masses of ice in the Gulf of Saint Lawrence while, just north of the Grand Banks, the ice flow splits with the current again, with about ten per cent of the ice and water sweeping around the southern tip of Newfoundland and heading for the Nova Scotian coast. The remaining ninety per cent turns southeast and east to eddy into oblivion.

In its passage south, the ice is not only at the mercy of the southward flow of the current; it is also subject to the direction of the wind and this, in turn, influences the fate of animals riding on the ice, particularly the seals. Offshore winds tend to scatter the floes which makes it difficult for seal hunters to find and

Southbound ice may be packed against the coast by onshore winds, and ▶ its passenger harp seals then become easy prey for hunting man's rifle.

catch their prey. But onshore winds pack the ice against the coast and whenever this happens, the shore people hunt. Such a wind drove such a mass of ice onshore in the thirties at St. John's, Newfoundland, one Saturday afternoon. Thousands of the city's residents ran out onto the ice, many of them from taverns and bars on the main street, for an opportunistic few hours of hunting at the city's front door.

The most dramatic manifestation of weather is, of course, the Maritime storm. One of the worst to hit the Grand Banks occurred on September 19, 1846. There is no accurate record of how many men died during the storm. Newfoundlanders, who must have been the hardest hit by it, simply had no means of collating the mortality figures from the scores of isolated outports and small fishing villages around the island. However, the port of Marblehead, in Massachusetts, kept a very good account of the disaster and erected a monument to it, inscribed: *The sea shall give up the dead that are in it*. Sixty-five men and boys from Marblehead went down in that one storm. Forty-three of them were family men and they left 155 fatherless children.

Another really tremendous storm was the Saxby Gale of October 4, 1869, which struck hardest into the Bay of Fundy region. It was named for a Lieutenant Saxby of the Royal Navy who, on the basis of what now we must assume to be intuition, predicted its arrival a year earlier. The gale, obviously a fall hurricane, wrecked miles of shoreline and uprooted entire coastal forests.

The key to the Atlantic region storm is almost always its unexpectedness. The people of Halifax may get a light snow warning, and then be buried under two feet of the stuff. One storm moved up the Nova Scotian coast a few years ago, and then veered into the gulf. The fishermen of Prince Edward Island, thinking it had passed the island, went fishing. Abruptly, the storm turned south, wrecked dozens of boats and drowned nearly forty men. Sudden storms, and the sandbars and currents of Sable Island have drowned about five thousand men, women and children there in three hundred years. More than two thousand fishermen from Lunenburg, a Nova Scotian fishing town with a population of about four thousand, have died in storms since the 18th century.

The weather of the Maritimes, so changeable and so unexpectedly violent at times, exacts its toll of wildlife as well.

Disasters to wildlife because of weather usually are hidden from human eyes but occasionally they occur on a scale that cannot be missed. On the night of December 20, 1925, Austin Squires, a New Brunswick ornithologist, recalls hearing a large flock of Canada geese milling in panic at night over the city of Fredericton during a snowstorm. The lights of the city probably had confused them and they were trying to get their bearings to the south or, at least, to safety. The geese are strong fliers and probably weathered the storm but on another occasion, December 18, 1903, a large flock ran into trouble at Chatham on their southern migration, and many of them smashed into trees and telephone lines.

Survivors of disasters are living clues to the nature of wild lives. A gale storm, particularly in the mid to late summer, leaves many inexperienced young seabirds wandering along shore beaches with broken wings and other injuries. The gulls are poorish fliers when they are young, so their plight is understandable, but less clear was the instance of 150 Leach's petrels, the Mother Carey's Chickens of sailors' stories, found piled dead along a beach at Holyrood in Newfoundland on the morning of June 6, 1941. Wilfred Templeman, a marine biologist from St. John's, found the bodies and conjectured that the petrels had been killed in a gale storm. But petrels are oceanic birds and tremendously powerful fliers. Their mass death suggests some other kind of disaster.

All seabirds, however, become victims of weather when, to use a nautical phrase, they "run out of sea room." They have the strength to ride out most storms as long as they have sea room. But at the coast, they may exhaust themselves trying, at any cost, to maintain their sea position. They may literally go to pieces. There are many examples of this among dovekies, small members of the auk family, which frequently are driven ashore in great numbers. They collapse in ponds, streams, even ditches, and offer no resistance when human beings pick them up. They, like all other forms of life along the Atlantic shore, have responded characteristically to their greatest enemy, the weather created by the often violent, always unexpected interaction of sea and shore. Climate is also a modifier of life, along with the geological nature of the land and the impact of the sea. It is, in fact, within the sea itself that some of the most important of these modifications take place.

A HISTORY OF CHANGE

The Atlantic provinces have been constantly changing throughout
their geological history. They lie in the northern segment of
the Appalachian system, a mountain range once as mighty as the
Rockies but reduced to its present shape by half-a-billion years
of erosion. Above, Percé starkly exhibits the erosive power of
the sea, the stack resulting from the collapse of a second arch.

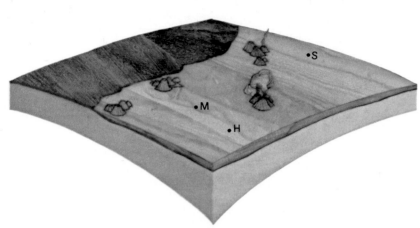

The sediments eroded from mountains of the Precambrian shield accumulated in a depression bordering the coastline. Volcanic islands also added their sediments to the trough and epeiric seas flooded the continent from ocean to ocean adding to the sediment accumulation during Cambrian times.

During the Ordovician period the increasing weight of sediments and forces within the earth depressed the earth's crust until it began cracking and bending, forming a new mountain range, the Appalachians. Increasingly active volcanoes along the shoreline contributed to the land-building process.

S — ST. JOHN'S
M — MONCTON
H — HALIFAX

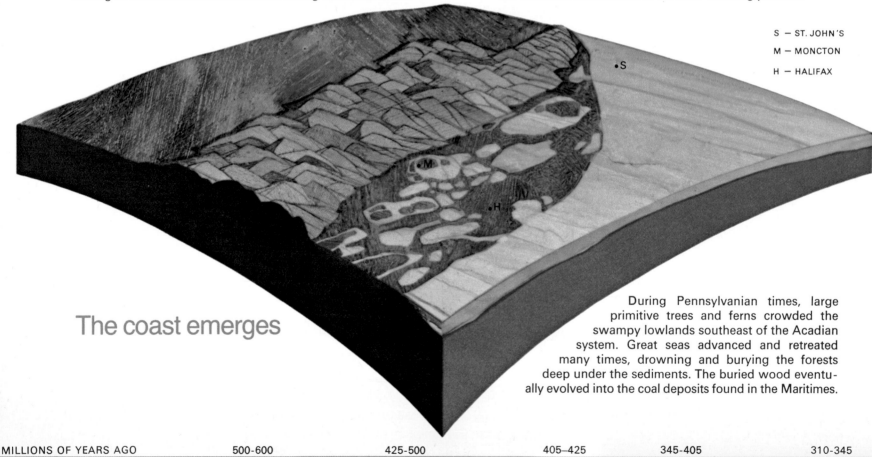

The coast emerges

During Pennsylvanian times, large primitive trees and ferns crowded the swampy lowlands southeast of the Acadian system. Great seas advanced and retreated many times, drowning and burying the forests deep under the sediments. The buried wood eventually evolved into the coal deposits found in the Maritimes.

MILLIONS OF YEARS AGO	500-600	425-500	405–425	345-405	310-345
CAMBRIAN		ORDOVICIAN	SILURIAN	DEVONIAN	MISSISSIPPIAN

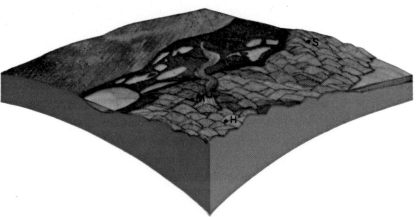

By Devonian time, basins once again filled with sediments. Erosion of the new Appalachian system was accompanied by new instability along the mountains' outer fringes. The northern part was intensely folded, faulted, and intruded with granites to become the Acadian Mountains.

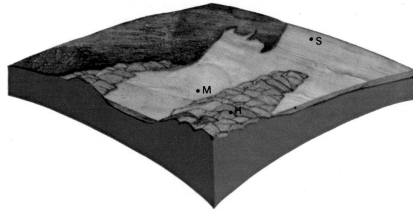

A constant cycle of uplift, erosion and deposition of sediments kept changing the shape of the Mountains. Normal faulting broke the crust of the earth into large blocks which formed the basic pattern of the Maritimes during the Mississippian era, 330 million years ago.

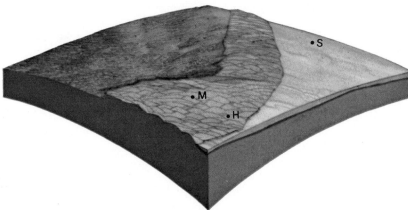

Erosion continued to smooth off the tops of mountains of the Acadian-Appalachian system. The east coast underwent few changes during Cretaceous times, while on the west coast mountains were being uplifted. The only sediments left from this period have accumulated on the continental shelf off Nova Scotia, and were discovered when oil borings were made in the sea floor to determine geological structure.

Pleistocene glaciers up to two miles thick advanced over the land in the Maritimes region and the adjacent sea floor, leaving moraines off the coast of Nova Scotia in 600 feet of water. As the climate warmed and the glaciers retreated, they left the earth's crust depressed far below its normal level. Ocean water flooded into the St. Lawrence River valley, drowning many of the low-lying coastal areas.

280-310	230–280	181–230	135–181	63–135	1–63	0–1
NNSYLVANIAN	PERMIAN	TRIASSIC	JURASSIC	CRETACEOUS	TERTIARY	QUATERNARY

LEPIDODENDRON

GIANT DRAGONFLY –
VEGANEURON

SCORPION (ALIVE)

SCORPION (DEAD)

AMPHIBIAN –
ASAPHESTERA PLARYRIS

LEPIDODENDRON

SIGILLARIA

CALAMITES

CLIMBING FERN

REPT
HYLONOMUS LYELLI

COCKROACH

Maritime coal deposits from Pennsylvanian times.

Record from the past

Through curious biological and geological cir-cumstances the Maritimes area has shed much light on the history of vertebrate animals. During the mild, wet Pennsylvanian period, luxurious vegetation filled the swamps, and trees related to club moss and horsetails grew up to a hundred feet high. Seas flooded again and again, burying the forests under sediments, and at Joggins, N.S. forty or fifty forests were piled atop each other. These became coal deposits. Hollow stumps left at the surface trapped animals, mostly amphib-ians, that eventually fossilized, but the most interesting fossils were of primitive reptiles, the oldest ever discovered. These reptiles were the first large animals to take the important step of laying their eggs on land. Insect life was highly evolved by this time, and giant dragonflies, large cockroaches, scorpions and spiders provided an abundant food supply for animals.

Sediments buried and killed the trees (1), left hollow stumps (2), trapping amphibians and rep-tiles (3) which were buried and later fossilized.

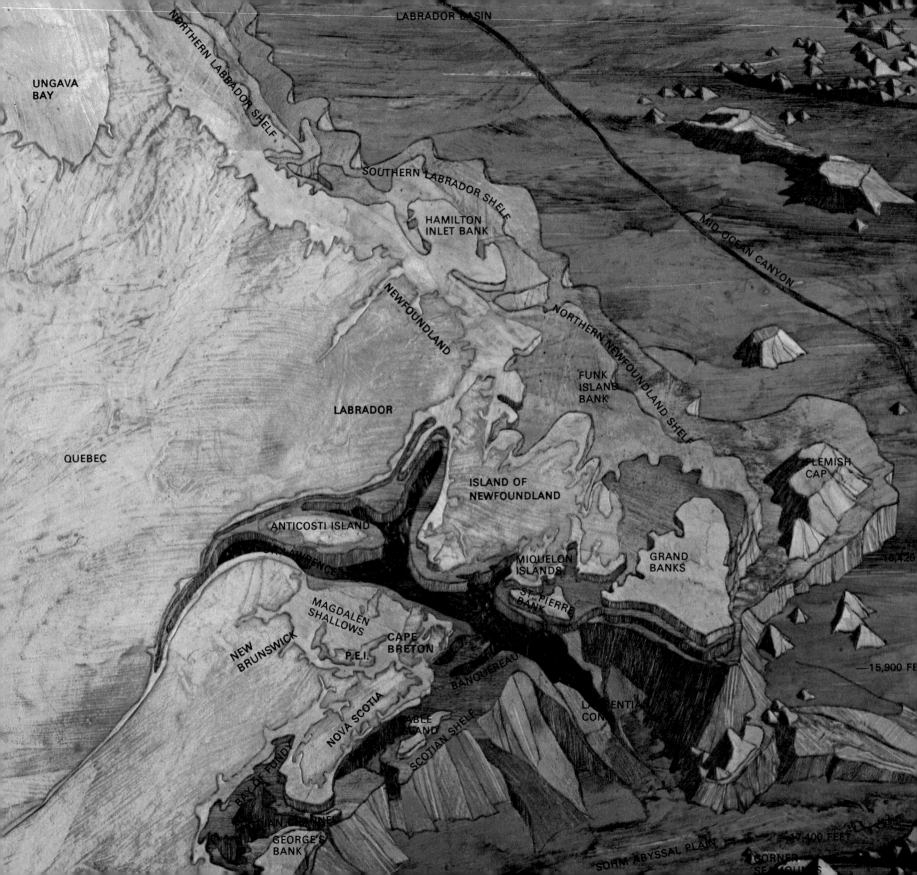

LABRADOR BASIN

UNGAVA
BAY

NORTHERN LABRADOR SHELF

SOUTHERN LABRADOR SHELF

MID-OCEAN CANYON

HAMILTON
INLET BANK

NEWFOUNDLAND

NORTHERN NEWFOUNDLAND SHELF

LABRADOR

FUNK
ISLAND
BANK

QUEBEC

FLEMISH
CAP

ISLAND OF
NEWFOUNDLAND

ANTICOSTI ISLAND

MIQUELON
ISLANDS

GRAND
BANKS

ST. LAWRENCE

ST-PIERRE
BANK

MAGDALEN
SHALLOWS

15,120

CAPE
BRETON

NEW
BRUNSWICK

P.E.I.

BANQUEREAU

15,900 FEET

LAURENTIAN
CON

NOVA SCOTIA

SABLE
ISLAND

SCOTIAN SHELF

BAY OF FUNDY

17,400 FEET

GEORGE'S
BANK

SOHM ABYSSAL PLAIN

CORNER
SE UNTS

Mountains in the deep

Beneath the oceans lies a landscape as rugged as any on earth. Until fairly recently it was thought that sediments deposited over millions of years had filled in the basins and buried the hills. With laying of transatlantic cables, research on the ocean floor began. An immense oceanic "spinal cord," the mid-Atlantic ridge, was found winding down the centre of the Atlantic with a deep trench along the central axis, criss-crossed by deep fractures and mountain chains. This is the largest single mountain system in the world, at least 10,000 miles long and 500 miles wide. Only rarely does a mountain peak break the ocean surface. Mt. Pico in the Azores towers 23,615 feet above the floor of the ocean and 7,613 feet above sea level. The deepest place is off Puerto Rico, 27,500 feet below sea level. The continental shelf, a vast underwater platform, surrounds the coastline, and extends into the North Atlantic. This platform is made up mostly of sediments and sedimentary rocks eroded from the continental interior and in places is 20,000 feet thick. The shelf has a width of seventy miles off the coast of northern Labrador broadening to 180 miles wide at the Grand Banks, one of the widest of all continental shelves. The depth of the water over the shelves increases gradually to 600 feet then increases more rapidly at the edge of the shelf. On the plateau of the Banks, most of the commercial fish of the world are found. Channels like the Fundian and the St. Lawrence Trough cut deeply into the continental shelves and into the continent itself, funnelling waters of deep oceanic origin close into the coast.

Eaten by the elements

The complex geology of the Atlantic coast has created an almost infinite variety of shorelines, each one constantly exposed to the erosive force of waves, currents and wind. No shoreline can remain static for long, and even the great rocky cliffs are constantly changed and reshaped. Beaches have been described as ''deposits of material which are in transit either along the shore, or off-and-on the shore.'' Three essential elements combine to make up a beach: a quantity of rocky material, a shoreline area into which it moves, and a supply of energy to move it. Sable Island and Percé are just two of of the ever-changing Maritimes shorelines.

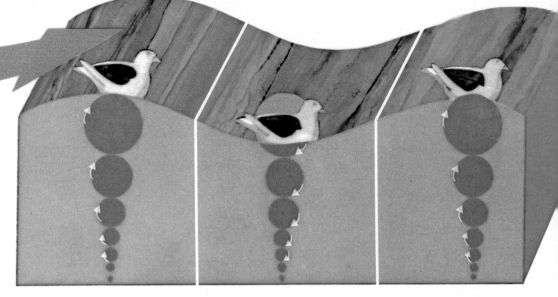

WIND DIRECTION

Surprisingly enough, waves and swells in deep water do not move the water horizontally; a bird would remain in one place without the effect of currents. Water particles in waves move forward in a circular motion under the crest and backward under the trough. This circular motion decreases in depth, disappearing at a depth of half the wave length.

Wave action can slowly alter rocky coastlines. Rivers cutting through the rocks make bays and irregular headlands. Waves hit the headlands with great force, but are dispersed in the bay.

As the headlands are slowly cut back by erosion, waves begin to form sand spits and bars along the eroded headland. This is the stage at which the coastline slowly begins to straighten out.

Eventually sand closes off the bay, creating a lagoon which is fed by inland streams helping to provide an environment for freshwater life.

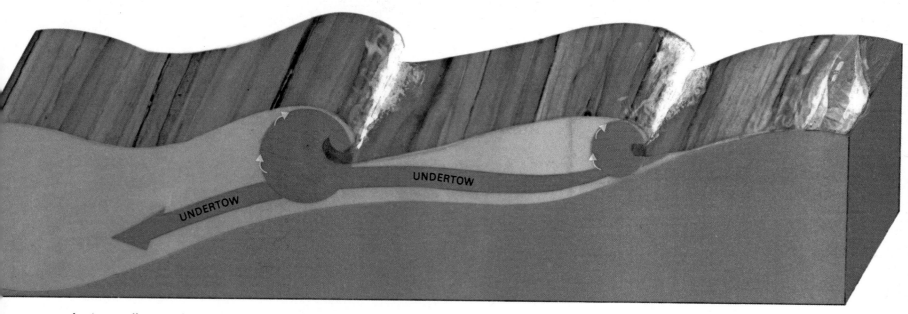

UNDERTOW

UNDERTOW

As the swell moves into shallow water, a remarkable change occurs. The waves are said to "feel" when the depth is half the wave length. The rising bottom compresses and heightens the wave, and it topples over. The force of a six-foot wave can be 3000 pounds per square foot.

The backwash from a wave flows down and under incoming waves, producing undertow. In summer, the backwash is often not strong enough to return all the sand brought landward and the beach is enlarged. In winter, larger waves move the sand back to the sea.

The erosive force of the sea can bore caves in the cliffs. If these caves are in a headland, tunnels will appear and eventually collapse, leaving a stack. Recession of the shoreline increases the distance of the stack from shore. Percé Rock illustrates this principle.

Killsite of an ancient culture

An exciting discovery was made in 1951 when artifacts of an ancient culture were found in the area of Camp Debert, Nova Scotia. Further excavations have unearthed over 4,000 artifacts from eleven living areas within the site, telling a fascinating tale of the paleo-Indians who hunted here around the year 8635 B.C. Modern-day archaeological and geological knowledge suggests the ancestral Asia-to-America crossing may have been an incredible 26,000 years ago, and that this killsite was used by Clovic man when retreating glacial ice was perhaps only 60 miles away, although it's likely that the climate was fairly warm. The quality of stone implements was improved by controlled application of heat, and most artifacts were found in or near hearths. Caribou were hunted with stone spears, their skins separated and cleaned with stone scrapers and perforated with stone awls before being fashioned into crude body-coverings.

All the stone tools were made from chalcedony, a variety of quartz, rather than flint. The spur (1) made perforations for tattooing or lacing. A slice of stone (2) served as a wedge to split bone. The point (3) of a spear was thinned by removing flakes from each side. Skins were cleaned by drawing an end scraper (4) across the hide.

Hopewell Caves in New Brunswick show
a superb example of a marine arch.

PART TWO / GEOLOGY

4 THE APPALACHIANS ARISE

The geological history of the Atlantic region is based on the creation of two main units that forged the Maritime environment. The first occurred sometime between the late Precambrian (about 700 million years ago) and the Devonian period (about 350 million years ago) when a broad seaway ran along the eastern border of the North American continent. Great masses of sediments were dropped, mainly by mud and sand, along with great piles of volcanic material.

The seas of the world were shallow then, and the land masses everywhere were low and undistinguished. Lichens sprouting among rocks and spore-bearing plants were the only land life. The great life development was occurring in the shallow, warm seas where, during 100 million years of almost changeless cosmos of climate and earth movement, single-celled forms of life grew to multi-celled, and the trilobite, which resembled the modern king crab, became the most successful form of life.

This great deposition of sediments went on uninterruptedly through the next two great geological periods, the Ordovician and the Silurian, interspersed with tremendous volcanic activity. The Ordovician saw the beginning of the building of the Appalachian system, a line of mountains rearing up from Alabama through Newfoundland. All these mountains parallel the coast and their development continued for about 300 million years (until 100 million years ago) when a large section of the earth's crust pushed in a roughly northwesterly direction against the bulk of the continent. This caused buckling and created what geologists call a northeast trending system.

The greatest deformation of the Atlantic region's rocks occurred, however, during the Devonian period when almost all the emplaced rocks were folded and faulted to produce a strong northeastern structural grain. This coincided with a steady rise out of the sea of all of eastern North America. By this time, rudimentary plants had colonized the land mass and a few scorpions and millipedes had joined them. The Devonian was a period of great life development throughout the Atlantic shore region. The land became green with large, tree-like plants; spiders abounded; the Appalachians likely rose as high as today's Alps

in the process of almost continual uplift.

However, the second important unit of geology in the Maritime region was not so violently affected by these events. This unit lies to the northwest of the Appalachian region and is called the Saint Lawrence platform, an immense body of Precambrian granitic and gneissic rocks nearly one billion years old. It is so old and so hard that it would not buckle or deform under the pressure of the westward-moving material. This formation can be seen all along the northern shores of the Gulf of Saint Lawrence, and in the Great North Peninsula of western Newfoundland.

In places, these old rocks, or "rigid crystalline basement rocks," as geologists call them, were overlaid with limestone and some shale and sandstone, remnants of which can be seen at Anticosti Island and at Mingan Island, on the gulf's north shore. These strata are mostly flat-lying and undeformed.

The westward-moving system overran the old hard rocks, particularly visibly in southwest Newfoundland, in the Humber Arm area, and in the northernmost part of the island, in the Hare Bay region. The rocks in both these areas are Appalachian –folded shale, sandstone and volcanics–which were thrust on and over the immovable Saint Lawrence platform.

The Devonian period, which saw shellfish swarming along all the northeastern coastlines, amphibians evolving, fishes dominating all oceanic life, plant life getting well established, also saw the appearance of large masses of granite magma which were intruded from folded rocks, at great depth, leaving traces which can be seen today in central and southern New Brunswick, Nova Scotia and central Newfoundland. This great intrusion, and the succeeding uplift, was a prelude to the erosion that has continued, more or less uninterrupted, until the present.

Through the Carboniferous and Permian periods, which followed the Devonian, the products of this erosion–detritus– were carried everywhere from the highland by active river systems and dumped in large quantities to form great sandstone deposits, and red, green and grey conglomerates. These can be seen in much of southern coastal Gaspé, in central and eastern New Brunswick, in northern Nova Scotia, and within western Newfoundland.

During the Carboniferous period, the seas flooded large flat coastal areas that were thickly forested; great coastal swamps were formed. In such ideal conditions, reptiles shucked off their need to breed in the sea and became permanently landbound. The forests were killed by the intruding sea or by rising swamp waters, and this laid down the Atlantic region's coal deposits.

These events formed about ninety per cent of all the rocks and structures which can be seen today in the Atlantic shore region. From the Permian period on, the main development was in the life forms, rather than in the earth substance. The Appalachians were eroded from about 15,000-foot peaks to low mountains of three to five thousand feet. As they eroded, the more adaptable conifers replaced the ancient scale trees; seed ferns and dinosaurs rose, and reptiles began flying.

One final geological event occurred during the Mesozoic era. A belt of non-marine red sediments, capped by a thick basalt flow, was formed at the Bay of Fundy, extending eastward to Chedabucto Bay. These are the youngest rocks exposed in the Appalachian land mass. The ultimate geological act of this ancient history, before the Pleistocene, was the mud and sand dumped over the Grand Banks and other banks areas throughout the Atlantic region. Over these were laid deposits from the last age, the Cenozoic, during the Tertiary and Pleistocene eras, when mammals become dominant, when men arose, and when four ice ages radically altered the physical appearance of the entire Atlantic shore region.

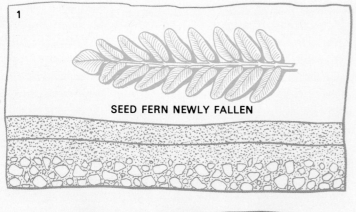

SEED FERN NEWLY FALLEN

PRESSURE

FORCED-OUT GASES

ABSORBED LIQUIDS

FORCED-OUT GASES

ABSORBED LIQUIDS

PRESSURE

The time trap

A type of fossilization called carbonization, or distillation, is especially effective in preserving the delicate structures of leaves and animals. A frond of a seed fern falling to the ground (1) is soon covered by sediments. Pressure from the weight of sediments on the leaf squeezes out the liquid and the gases (2). All that is left behind is a thin, filmy residue consisting mostly of carbon, but this kind of fossilization is so delicate that fine veins of leaves and even the individual cell walls of the fern are preserved (3). Sometimes the film of carbon can be stripped from the rock and mounted for display.

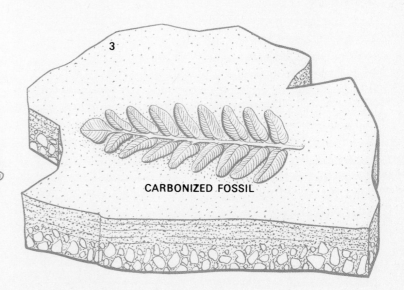

CARBONIZED FOSSIL

5 AN ICE AGE STEALS THE SOIL

During the waning years of the Pleistocene geological age, great quantities of fire clay were deposited over the bottom of the sea southeast of Newfoundland. In these deposits were minerals, chlorite, montmorillonite and illite. A sharp concussion can shatter this mineral mixture into such tiny pieces that it is transformed into a thick liquid.

These Pleistocene deposits remained undisturbed until the 20th centry, when a submarine earthquake, centered at the edge of the continental shelf, occurred in the 1930's. The concussion fled along the sea bottom and through the water, instantly liquifying a submarine mass 230 miles wide, and beginning the largest landslide in man's history.

The submarine avalanche rumbled on in a southeasterly direction, into the abyssal depths of the Atlantic, maintaining a steady fourteen miles an hour, a speed computed from its destruction of twelve transatlantic telephone cables. Thirty hours after the earthquake, the avalanche ended about four hundred miles from its birthplace.

This avalanche is a rare example of an immediately-visible geological change, and it is typical of the Pleistocene, the last, and most drastic, of the geological ages since it compressed great changes into a relatively short period of time—only about one million years.

The Pleistocene era followed the Miocene and Pliocene which were the ages of grasslands spreading, of the Rockies being uplifted, of large carnivores and the first man-apes. At the beginning of the Pleistocene, the climate of the Atlantic region began to change from moderate-cool to winters that were longer and colder. Eventually, snow lay all year in sheltered valleys. (Even today, snow sometimes sits on the sunless sides of Newfoundland hills until late June.) Within a few thousand years, the region was covered with a blanket of snow the year round. Gradually, the snow thickened and the lower layers turned to ice. The weight of the overburdening snow and ice squeezed the bottom layers so that they began to move down hills and into valleys. This was the ice cap which can be seen, in the same form, in Greenland today. The movement was im-perceptible but irresistibly destructive, like a great, slow sheet of sandpaper being pushed across the land.

In Newfoundland, where the process began early and ended late, almost nothing remained untouched by this movement of ice. Billions of tons of soil were stripped from the surface and carried away. In some places it was later dumped hundreds of feet deep. Everywhere, bedrock was exposed by the grinding action, and then polished smooth by the movement of the ice. Ranges of hills were rounded off, and inlets running into the sea were bulldozed deeper, wider, steeper. This was particularly true along the southern shore of Newfoundland where, 20,000 years later, these inlets became sanctuaries for humans who lived and hunted at the entrances in summer, and then retired to the sheltered interiors of the inlets during winter.

It is not surprising, therefore, that some geologists call Newfoundland a monument to glaciation. Its rocky 43,359 square miles are pockmarked with thousands of lakes and ponds which themselves cover nearly 2,200 square miles. Its valleys have been sculptured into characteristic shapes; everywhere rocky mounds and knobs show the influence of thousands of years of passing ice. The long lakes, Grand, Red Indian, Gander and Deer, reflect the general orientation of the Appalachian system. When the ice was flowing outward from the island, it ground down the major river systems—like the Gander and the Exploits—which run northeast, and along the shorter, smaller southern rivers which run south and often have their headwaters only a few miles from the northerly-flowing rivers. Western-flowing ice ran down the Humber, the only river to reach the west coast of Newfoundland. The island's major mountains, the Long Range, are uplifted, eroded, twisted and glaciated remnants of once-extensive plain-lands. The table-top peaks are monuments to the vastness and weight of the ancient icefields which sought to grind them flat.

At the height of the ice age, about 40,000 years ago, the ice had sopped up so much sea-water within its giant, smothering cap that sea-water levels were lowered between three hundred and four hundred feet below the present levels. This massive withdrawal of the sea lasted until about 19,000 years ago and created hundreds of islands spattered along the Scotian shelf, while expanding the sliver of Sable Island into a relatively large one. It created channels and lagoons along the coast.

At the peak of the Pleistocene, the ice sheet very likely pushed right across the Scotian shelf, grinding its way over the very old Ordovician rocks. At least once during the ice advance, or retreat, the glacier paused long enough to drop a long line of moraine (or glacial rubbish) that stretched roughly from Halifax (at that point about thirty-five kilometers offshore) for about five hundred kilometers parallel to the coastline. A similar moraine, which can be seen above ground, traverses Long Island, Martha's Vineyard, Nantucket and Cape Cod.

As the ice withdrew from the Scotian shelf, it initially left dry land onto which poured trees, plants and animals. There is some evidence, further south, that man hunted deer, walrus and other animals on this offshore strip of dry land which stretched almost unbroken from Cape Cod to Newfoundland, and it was a likely road for the migration of some immediate, post-glacial migrations of plants and animals. But as the melting of the ice continued, the sea rose gradually. The offshore banks, complete with their river systems, their forests, deer herds, beaches and rocky shorelines, were slowly drowned. The Atlantic waves, marching inland, brought sediments winnowed from offshore, from beaches and river beds, and dumped them in the old river beds. In some places the sediment completely covered all evidence of glacial activity.

This was a time when fine marine clays were moved back and forth, when gravels were sifted clear of sediment and laid down, when all the conditions for the rich fishing grounds of a few thousand years later were established.

A cross-section of a typical banks area anywhere in the Atlantic region might show a channel (a former river valley) cut into Tertiary or Cretaceous rocks, about six hundred feet deep and about three miles wide. It would look like many of the small river valleys one can see in Nova Scotia and New Brunswick today. At the bottom of the channel, a solid mass of three hundred feet of glacial drift would be deposited. This would be overlaid by another two hundred feet of silt, doubtless dropped by hovering icebergs and icepans.

The ice was so thick and so heavy that it depressed the land, especially in places where there was no hard layer of old Cambrian or Precambrian rock to resist its enormous weight. It made an island out of Nova Scotia by pushing down the *chignecto isthmus* several hundred feet. As the ice melted between

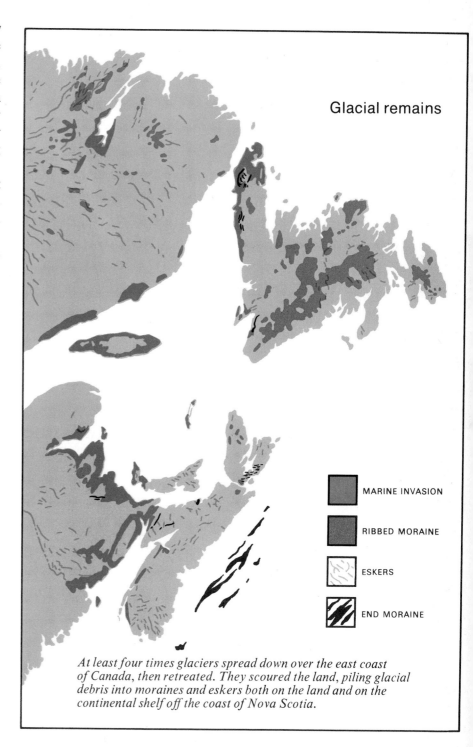

Glacial remains

MARINE INVASION

RIBBED MORAINE

ESKERS

END MORAINE

At least four times glaciers spread down over the east coast of Canada, then retreated. They scoured the land, piling glacial debris into moraines and eskers both on the land and on the continental shelf off the coast of Nova Scotia.

Saint John and Fredericton, the sea moved in along the sunken land (what is now the St. John River valley) to create an estuary almost as far north as Woodstock. The ice appears to have halted briefly at Woodstock, and then advanced to drop several hundred feet of gravels. Later, these gravels were flushed down the St. John River to form a series of river terraces.

The withdrawal of the ice was neither straightforward nor rapid. Thousands of years elapsed as the ice receded here a little, advanced there a little, receded again. In many places, large areas of brackish water were formed along the coast as the ice, gone from the outer banks regions, continued to dump large quantities of fresh water into inshore shallows. These lagoons were more like inland seas, containing their own forms of freshwater life.

When the ice finally disappeared, it left behind a series of barren vistas into which vegetation struggled with difficulty. It took hundreds of years to establish trees in some areas (thousands in parts of Newfoundland) and in many areas the trees never could get a foothold.

The footnote to the Pleistocene glaciation is simple for much of the Atlantic region: the age stole the region's soil and dumped it in deep Atlantic waters.

The emplacement of rocks in pre-Pleistocene times was critical to modern man's affairs since the distribution arbitrated what plants, animals and insects live where and in what numbers. For instance, soils that result from complex mixtures of crystalline and metamorphic rocks are richer than those that result from sedimentary rocks. Soils resulting from Devonian granite, Precambrian quartzite and hard Mississippian sandstone are almost always coarse, infertile and shallow. In such environments, only conifers or the toughest pioneering trees, like aspens, grey and white birch and red maple, can hope to gain entry.

Sometimes, the environment is created by the deposition of glacial matter; sometimes by the interaction of the soil on top and the rocks immediately beneath. Heavy soils emplaced above horizontal strata of Carboniferous shales, sandstones and conglomerates, with their low fertility and bad drainage, create an environment for conifers and tolerant hardwoods only. If, however, the strata are tilted, or tipped, particularly at a steep angle, an entirely different opportunity for vegetation is created.

Drainage is usually good because the water can escape down the tilt lines. Sugar maple, beech, and yellow birch will thrive on the upper slopes and hilltops of such formations; hardwoods and mixed woods will thrive in the lower areas where there are tilted shales.

The nature of the geology dictates the environment, and the Atlantic region is alternately blessed and cursed by this fact. If the Pleistocene had not ground down so hard and so long, the region might be a moderately rich one for agriculture. If, on the other hand, the region had not been so thoroughly deformed, twisted, and broken up by geological pressures, it would not proffer anywhere near the mineral wealth that is being exploited today. The deformation thrust up a diversity of geological environments that is one of the fascinations, and frustrations, to the student of Atlantic region geology. It is almost impossible to make generalizations about the area.

One generalization *is* possible. Most of the soils are podzols. The name is derived from a Russian word meaning ash-like soil, and refers to the soil's color. The podzols are caused by heavy rain, long cold winters, short summers, and the work of forest cover. They are thought to be created when percolating water removes the easily soluble substances from the surface, washing away the nutrients. Then the cold cuts down the work of the decay-making micro-organisms. As a result, plant remains accumulate at the surface as raw humus. The end product is raw humus at the top, an ash-like layer in the middle, and a reddish-brown mixture of precipitated humus and sesquioxides at the bottom.

The Annapolis Valley of Nova Scotia, by far the richest soil area in the province, has podzolic soils which are actually quite low in fertility and will sustain only certain crops, particularly apples. Even the deep Prince Edward Island red soils are not particularly fertile, and produce only specialist crops like potatoes and strawberries.

Newfoundland is the worst served of all, since most of the island's soil developed from ice-scoured rock as shallow as half an inch, as deep as eighteen inches. The chemicals essential to make fertile soil, nitrogen, phosphorous, potassium and calcium are only meagrely present.

Much of central New Brunswick and southwestern Nova Scotia are cursed geologically with Devonian granite that

Barrenlands, such as this vast area at Avalon Peninsula, Newfoundland, were one result of the Pleistocene Ice Age, which stole much soil and left behind massive rocks and boulders; repeated fires, too, killed off most of the vegetation which had struggled to regain a foothold in the region.

creates shallow, coarse and stony soils which leach easily and get rapidly poorer as the rainfall increases. A layer of clay, hardened by iron, frequently forms under this soil, usually making it permanently useless for good growth.

If, however, the granite is mixed with other hard rocks, and this occurs in the Cobequid and Caledonia Mountains, the soil is made much more resistant to leaching and is rich in nutrients.

Another curse of the Atlantic region is the barrens which occur in large areas of Nova Scotia and Newfoundland. Some barrens, especially in Newfoundland, have been caused by fire that repeatedly killed off all tree growth. Elsewhere, as in south-west Nova Scotia, barrens may be the natural environment of shallow, coarse, acid, rocky ground. Such barrens are also victims of the glacial period which formed a tight-packed permafrost layer very close to the surface. In the thin, loose soil above the layer, a thick growth of huckleberry took over, with a dense but superficial rooting system that kept out almost all other growth. The litter mass acidifies rainwater which picks up

humic acids and extracts iron from the soil, then moves down and stops at the permafrost layer, thus forming an even more impermeable pan.

The barrens are strange places for human beings and they affect some people the way the desert and the Arctic do. In some barren lands, the Pleistocene not only took away the soil and deposited a permafrost layer, it also left the lands strewn with massive rocks and boulders which give the topography an eerie beauty. The late and post-glacial action of freezing and thawing opened up large cracks in the rocky underpinning of the barrens. These cracks, wedged open by ice, formed hummocks and knolls and mounds. As the permafrost disappeared, the action of the frost moved boulders down into the cracklines to form weird, angular patterns of jumbled rocks.

Soil is, of course, the most fundamental wealth of any region, and its paucity in the Maritimes is the reason for the small populations of people and the general difficulty the provinces have had in matching the economic and social gains made

47

elsewhere in Canada. They are relatively rich, however, in some minerals. When the French were building the fortress of Louisburg on Cape Breton Island two hundred years ago, they mined coal from what is now called the Sydney field nearby. This field, and others of Pennsylvanian strata at Pictou and Cumberland counties on mainland Nova Scotia, as well as at Minto in New Brunswick, have subsequently yielded millions of tons of coal.

The coal is a gift of the Carboniferous geological period. It was given generously to Cape Breton, rather less generously to Springhill and Joggins, in Nova Scotia, and to a few spots in Newfoundland. There are great deposits of lead and zinc in the Buchans region of Newfoundland; even greater orebodies in the Bathurst-Newcastle region of New Brunswick.

The Appalachian region is packed with occurrences of iron ore. The greatest and most accessible body is on Newfoundland's Belle Isle. It produces around two million tons of ore a year. There is manganese in Nova Scotia and New Brunswick; antimony at Moretons Harbour, Newfoundland, West Gore, Nova Scotia, and Lake George, New Brunswick; tungsten in Halifax county, Nova Scotia; vanadium in Newfoundland; titanium at St. Georges Bay, Newfoundland; tin at New Ross, Nova Scotia; oil and natural gas near Moncton, New Brunswick; large deposits of gypsum in the Windsor district of Hants County, Nova Scotia; as well as elsewhere in the Maritimes.

During the Triassic period, a time of sedimentation and active volcanoes, great quantities of volcanic rocks containing agate, jasper and zeolites were deposited in the Bay of Fundy region, making it a popular area for rock and gemstone hunters. In the Gaspé Peninsula and northern New Brunswick, the rock-hunter finds another rich area for his collecting. Chalcedony and jasper are common along the Gaspé, and in Chaleur Bay, and the shoreline of New Brunswick, from Campbellton to Bathurst, yields jasper, agates, zeolites and fossils. Topaz, fluorite, beryl and other minerals occur near Napadogan.

But for the amateur observer walking this varied environment, it is the poverty of the soil rather than the wealth of the minerals that remains in his memory. He may walk the barrens, his feet brushing broom crowberry, huckleberry, blueberry, laurel, sarsaparilla, inkberry, bayberry, witherrod, with here and there a stunted black spruce making its entrance, and feel the proximity of the ice age so recently past.

6 TIDES AND CURRENTS

There are 35,000 cubic miles of water in the Gulf of Saint Lawrence, and the entire contents of the gulf are changed every two years and four months. They are flushed away by a triple combination of water pushing down from a watershed beginning 2,000 miles away, beyond the banks of Lake Superior, by the coriolis effect of the turning earth, and by manifold currents.

These currents are dominated by a portion of the Labrador Current, born in the Arctic, by the Gaspé Current which, with one hundred times the flow of the Saint Lawrence River, hugs the Gaspé coast and then drops down over the Magdalen Shallows, and by a submarine current which runs west along the Laurentian Channel.

Currents reflect earth systems of cosmic proportions. A winter of heavy snow in Antarctica can cool the waters of the central Atlantic seven years later. The Labrador Current, in all its majesty, may serve as a model for this kind of influence. It is a great escape valve for the Arctic and a dictator of nearly all life in the Maritime region. Arctic water, circulating over hundreds of thousands of square miles, cannot escape along the Russian front and very little of it moves through the Bering Straits. Its main escape route is down the east coast of Greenland, thence to Labrador, Newfoundland, and ultimately to a collision with the Gulf Stream at the Grand Banks.

The current comes south in two fairly distinct lines of force. One line hugs the shore and a portion of it forces into Hudson's Bay across the top of the Labrador Peninsula. A part of the same force, nearly one thousand miles to the south, pushes through the Strait of Belle Isle and heads into the Gulf of Saint Lawrence.

The other line of force is mostly west Greenland current water which moves southward further offshore at a little more than half a mile an hour. As it reaches the edge of the Grand

Borne by icy currents coursing southward from the Arctic, icebergs ▶
sail down the Labrador Sea around the north coast of Newfoundland.

Banks, the inshore division of it turns southwest. Some of it may even penetrate the Cabot Strait and enter the southern end of the Gulf of Saint Lawrence where, conceivably, its waters could mix with the Labrador Current water of the Strait of Belle Isle.

This great Arctic current, 1300 feet deep and from ten to twenty miles wide, theoretically should give the south a whiff of lifeless ice waters. Instead, it is packed with enriching mineral salts and planktonic animals feeding on them which makes it a feeding territory for countless larger forms of life.

Meanwhile, the great "river in the sea," as the Gulf Stream has been called, moves in its clockwise circulation of the North Atlantic towards a collision with the Labrador. It meanders along. Sometimes its northern edge may be only 250 miles from Halifax, Nova Scotia, while at other times, it may be 500 miles offshore. It, too, contains much life but it is nowhere near as rich as the Labrador. In its friction with colder waters, it spins off odd southern forms of life into the Maritime system.

Finally, in the Grand Banks region, the two currents collide. It is the irresistible object meeting the immovable force. Across great areas of sea "cabelling" occurs. This is an oceanographic phenomenon caused by submarine pressures which send water bubbling and leaping up along the line of collision. A biological reaction begins. Plankton, the microscopic marine animals and plants, begin breeding in reaction to the mixing of cold and warm waters, and to the infusion of mineral foods. Feeding on this planktonic population explosion are many small fish–capelin, herring, small cod and haddock–and feeding on them are the adult fish: legions of cod, haddock, pollack and others. Again, preying on them are whales, sharks, swordfish, and finally, preying on everything are thousands of fishermen from a dozen countries.

The movement of currents may continue unseen and unmeasured for hundreds of miles. Although the Labrador may seem to die in the vicinity of the Grand Banks, and to peter out in the Gulf of Saint Lawrence, its effect ranges further. Occasionally, the Bay of Fundy is invaded by Arctic or far northern life forms carried in the dying extremities of the Labrador Current. These include capelin which live almost solely in Newfoundland and northern waters. Arctic plankton has reached Fundy, and even Arctic white whales, belugas, have been seen disporting themselves in the Passamaquoddy region. The nearest belugas occur in the ice-cold waters of the Saint Lawrence estuary at the mouth of the Saguenay.

The Gulf Stream also creates involuntary movements of life. In 1951, a great ocean sunfish was taken on the Fundy coast west of Saint John. Several tropic jellyfish, the dreaded Portuguese man o'war, have been taken in Passamaquoddy Bay. Tropical floating tunicates are thrust into Fundy in swarms. They die there and are cast up on beaches.

The entire Marine area is a maelstrom of currents, large and small, many of them, as the mariners' guide, *Blunt's Pilot,* notes, "flowing against the wind." In the early days their complexities could only be learned through recurrent disasters. The Labrador Current, for instance, deflected early mariners from their courses and, although their navigation might be exemplary, they found themselves willy-nilly on the sands of Sable Island. Once in the region of Sable, they became victims of a wild mixture of contrary currents that almost always took them to their destruction.

There was no way for the early sailors to know that one reason for their plight was a well-nigh unbelievable action of the Labrador Current. The section of the current passing through the Strait of Belle Isle into the Gulf of Saint Lawrence collides with the outflow of the Saint Lawrence River. Then it passes into the open sea through the Straits of Canso, colliding now with the Grand Banks-Gulf Stream deflection of the Labrador Current in the vicinity of Sable Island.

It is small wonder, in the words of a 19th century clergyman, the Rev. George Patterson, that "currents round the island are terribly conflicting and uncertain, sometimes being in the opposite direction to the prevailing winds, and sometimes passing round the whole circuit of the compass in twenty-four hours. As currents of water, like currents of air meeting from different directions, produce eddies, these produce marvelous swirls round the island. An empty cask will be carried round and round the island, making the circuit several times, and the same is the case with bodies from wrecks."

The force of the currents, and of the waves, is slowly moving Sable eastward. The western tip of the island is almost constantly being worn away. Between 1766 and the year 1899 when Alexander Graham Bell visited the island in search of the bodies of friends lost in a shipwreck, the island moved six miles. It

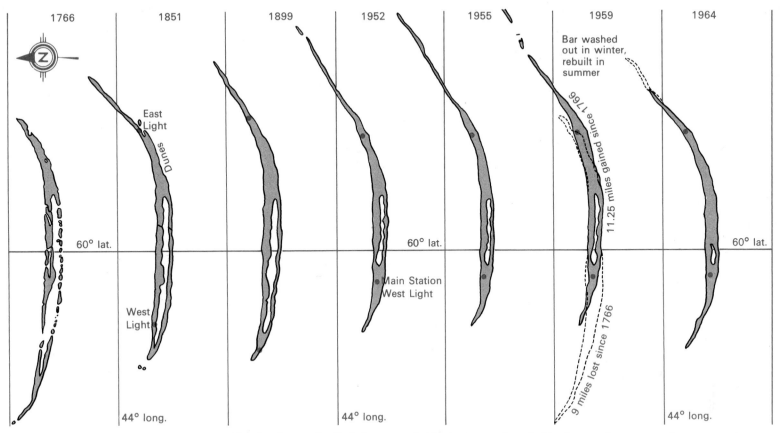

1766   1851   1899   1952   1955   1959   1964

East
Light

Dunes

60° lat.   60° lat.   60° lat.

West
Light

Bar washed
out in winter,
rebuilt in
summer

11.25 miles gained since 1766

Main Station
West Light

9 miles lost since 1766

44° long.   44° long.   44° long.

As shown in this sequence of drawings, Sable Island is gradually being extended in the east and eroded in the west by waves and current action. Serious erosion losses happen during severe storms, but one of the greatest threats to its continued existence is the slowly rising sea level.

seems to be moving and breaking up at a slower rate today.

All currents and tides work with majestic leisure and their workings are not immediately visible to man's eye. This is especially true of storm surges which occasionally have odd effects in the Atlantic shore region. These surges travel outward in all directions from the center of any storm and superficially they resemble miniature tsunami, or tidal waves. The storm surge wave, if it can be named as positively that, is solitary. It takes almost an hour to build up to its peak and then subsides in about the same time. Rarely are storm surges noticed anywhere, unless they happen to coincide with extra high tides. At Margaree Harbor, Cape Breton, for instance, a recent storm surge raised the tide level by seven feet, a local phenomenon which never made the news. But if such a surge had occurred in

Halifax Harbour, or in the Bay of Fundy at high tide, it would have been international news.

The storm surge has a junior brother whose origin is unknown. It takes the form of tidal wiggles (for want of a better description) which unaccountably raise water levels from six to twelve inches. The wiggles may lift the water in a few minutes, and subside as abruptly, usually within fifteen minutes. They are quite common in the Bay of Fundy, and there is no explanation for them at this time.

The tides of the Bay of Fundy are famous for their size but the entire bay is an engine of energetic currents. The bay is constantly subjected to the twisting effect, the Coriolis Force, caused by the rotation of the earth which tends to throw the water in a counter-clockwise direction. It pushes water steadily along the Nova Scotian coast, around the head of the bay, and west along the New Brunswick shore. This movement is distorted by the outflow of the New Brunswick rivers.

Yet another force, the wind, exerts its added influence. It blows persistently from the southwest in seasons when the rivers are low in drought. It can seal off the mouth of the bay and the water inside rotates endlessly without renewal from the Gulf of Maine. Plankton populations are decimated and plankton feeders starve. Herring may migrate hundreds of miles in search of new feeding pastures and being unable to spawn satisfactorily, entire year classes may die out.

The closed system may help shellfish. When scallops spawn, their billions of eggs usually twist out of the bay and most die in the open ocean. Trapped in the bay by the wind, they can hatch in great numbers.

The movement of the tide in the Minas Basin of Fundy is only a little less dramatic than the reversing falls on the northern side of the bay. As pressure builds up and the funnelling effect takes over, the water begins to pour round the end of Cape Split, protruding into the bay, creating a large area of softly roaring waters heading into the basin. An optical illusion is created; the entire visible bay seems tilted slightly and the water appears to be running downhill. As the water pours into the basin, the bulk of it is concealed in a fairly deep channel. What is visible over thousands of acres of sand and mud flats is an inexorably advancing ripple of waves. The Coriolis Force does not work in the basin. Floating material, the branches of trees, fishing buoys, the wreckage of boats, accumulates at the mouth of the channel in a dense mass known locally as the "cedar swamp." Deep in the channel some cod, haddock, hake and halibut are taken into the basin area. Once the tide turns, however, there are dark and mysterious turns and overturns of water which are dangerous to fishing vessels. Deep sea sailors penetrating the basin at high tide to get gypsum cargoes at Parrsboro have reported seeing entire trees and telegraph poles up-ended in the middle of this outgoing tide and sucked down in whirlpools. No man, woman or child, lost in boat, bathing or bridge-building accidents has ever been recovered from a Minas Basin drowning.

The great tides gave the early settlers an idea of how to use them to catch fish. The withdrawing tide drained great areas of mud and sandflats—150 square miles in the Minas Basin alone—

so the early fishermen emplaced permanent nets or traps and allowed the fish to catch themselves as the tide withdrew. The Acadian French on the Nova Scotian side of the bay first used the scheme, with such success that it was copied by the New Brunswickers in the early 1820's. Many traps, some of them miles long, are still in use.

All the waters of the Maritimes are subjected to the frictional force of wind which in extreme cases can pile up water feet deep along resisting shorelines, flood inlets, coves and bays, and even partially back up rivers. Everywhere, wind sets water in motion so that a strong southerly wind may be driving Labrador Current surface water northward while beneath, the main body of water is still flooding south.

The force of the wind is transmitted to the water through friction, and as it moves the surface layers, the friction also moves lower levels, although at a much slower rate because of the inefficient transference of energy.

When persistent easterlies blow in shallow water, particularly across the warm Magdalen Shallows in the southern part of the Gulf of Saint Lawrence, they push the surface waters against the distant shores of New Brunswick. The water, trapped against the shore, doubles back under itself, creating a large submarine counter-current. When this is powerful enough, it can obliterate entire populations of shellfish. Scallops, particularly, cannot tolerate the warmer temperature of surface water thrust so unexpectedly among them.

Scallop mortalities are only one measurement of the effects of these submarine currents. It is easy to conjecture about their effects on other forms of life, particularly codfish which are most intolerant of warm water. Codfish, feeding in some deep valley, might easily find themselves trapped in marine graveyards by overburdening warm waters. Many fish, in their drifting larval forms, are completely at the mercy of currents, and if these currents do not flow conventionally, they can kill entire year classes of creatures. Such disasters are relative. They seem disastrous to man's eye and overshadow the more important work that is going on in the background. The currents transport life on a huge scale. They bring the Arctic travellers south and push the equatorial creatures north. They are the highways of the sea along which life perpetually probes and challenges the possibilities for new forms of expression.

THE SEA–BASIS OF LIFE

The fascinations of the sea have long attracted man; many a salty
tale of battling sea-demons has been set in the Atlantic region.
Here we discover a drama of infinite life; of intricate food-webs woven
by hordes of tiny creatures such as the mysid above; of colliding
currents and tides, oceanic highways, enshrouding fogs and lashing
gales–a cyclical drama of life and death continuing forever.

Unseen elements ▪ ▪ ▪

The Atlantic coast of Canada has long been famous for its rich and varied fishing grounds, winds and currents contributing to the abundance. All currents are ultimately wind-driven, so that any changes in wind systems bring changes to currents and to all marine life. Two major current systems reach the Maritimes. From the north, the Labrador Current carries cold water of relatively low salinity down the coastline. Cold water can hold more oxygen than warm water, and consequently this Arctic current is packed with plankton feeding on its nutrients. From the south, the warm fast-flowing Gulf Stream heads towards Newfoundland, containing much life, spinning off the odd southern animal into the Maritimes. Just off the southern tip of the Grand Banks, the great Labrador and Gulf Stream Currents collide, pressure causes the waters to bubble and leap, sweeping up to the surface water and mineral salts from the bottom. Both the mixing of cold and warm waters and the infusion of minerals stimulate the plankton into rampant breeding, which in turn attracts larger marine animals into the area to eat the food so richly supplied by the planktonic explosion. Currents are truly highways of the sea, transporting marine life on a grand scale. Even fish in their drifting larval forms are at the mercy of these currents.

The weather map illustrates the movements of air and circulation of currents in the North Atlantic. The interaction of these two climatic forces that are both continental and oceanic creates banks of fog, dense enough to cut visibility to zero.

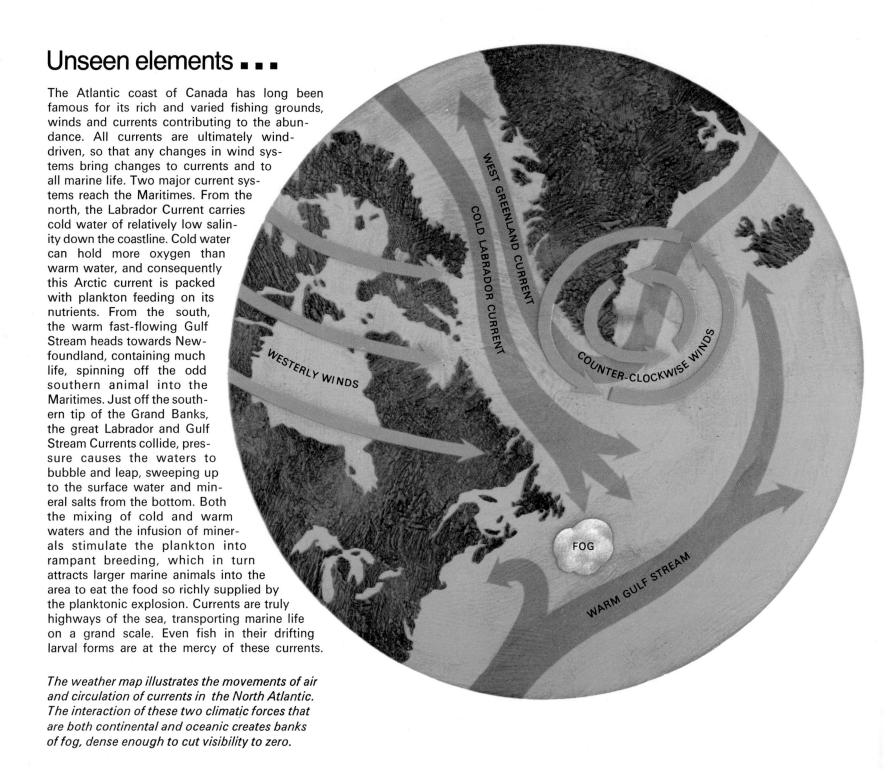

provide sustenance ▪ ▪ ▪

General abundance of plankton in the North Atlantic region in light, medium and heavy concentrations is illustrated here. In indescribable variety, hordes of plankton drift and float, taking advantage of the excellent environment provided by a collision of the

HEAVY CONCENTRATION

MEDIUM CONCENTRATION

LIGHT CONCENTRATION

great Labrador and Gulf Stream Currents. Tons of enriching nutrients such as phosphates and nitrates accumulate on the sea bottom, and upswelling currents carry them to the surface providing a rich food source for these tiny creatures. Oxygen supply in the water is increased by the crashing and splashing of the waves, and a temperate zone preferred by plankton is created by the mingling of cold and warm waters.

for life in the sea

An abundance of plankton and extensive areas of relatively shallow water help make the Maritimes one of the world's best fishing areas. The population of herring alone has been estimated at around 75 billion fish, and nearly 600 million pounds of cod are taken

ST. PIERRE BANK

GRAND BANK

MISAINE BANK

CANSO BANK

BANQUEREAU BANK

SAMBRO BANK

SABLE ISLAND BANK

BROWNS BANK

annually. On the map of the ocean floor (page 34) the Atlantic provinces, especially Newfoundland, are surrounded by wide, gently sloping platforms with water averaging about 300 feet. Fish concentrate over these shelves, where the water is layered in combinations of salinity and temperature. The occurrence and concentration of fish schools depend on this layering effect, and the fishing industry is a mainstay in the economy.

Manna of the sea

The profusion of marine life begins with tiny plants and animals, up to 20 million of them living in a cubic foot of seawater. Basic to any food chain are bacteria, microscopic organisms that can live on inorganic material and make it useful to the organic world of plants and animals. Smallest among the drifting life of the sea is the nannoplankton (1). Diatoms (2) dinoflagellates (3) and naked flagellates (4) are simple plant forms continually adding oxygen to the sea through photosynthesis. Dinoflagellates have a single-celled body armoured with an envelope of cellulose. A great variety of animal plankton feed on these plants. Even simple animals, like the protozoa (5) show diversity; some are free-swimming, some form colonies that can even show a division of labour, and some are parasitic (6). The crustaceans are highly-developed animals when compared to the protozoa. Copepods (6) and euphasids (7) are planktonic throughout their lives, while other crustaceans spend only the larval stages as plankton (8, 9, 11, 12, 13) before growing into larger animals. Still others become plankton only in an adult phase such as the medusa of the hydroid (10). These and an infinite variety of others supply the life line for the animals of the sea.

With the setting sun, these copepods ● , jellyfish ○ , fairy shrimp △ , rise to feed in the surface darkness. As daylight approaches, they sink again to darker regions.

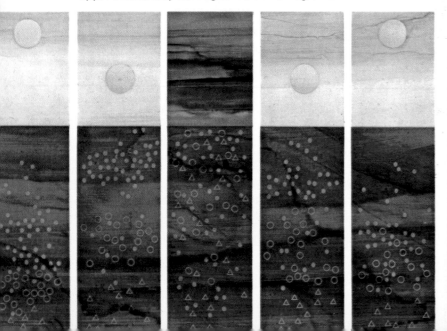

TOP VIEW

SIDE VIEW

1

2

LOCOMOTION PLATE

SPINE

NORMAL PLATE

a

b

c

Diatoms reproduce by division of the nucleus (a), cell walls form (b), and the diatom splits into two unequal pieces (c).

NANNOPLANKTON

DIATOMS

ARMOURED DINOFLAGELLATE

VORTICELLA COLONY

ADULT STAGE OF HYDROID
10

EUPHASID 7

3

5

STARFISH LARVA 11

4

6

CRAB LARVA 8

PHOSPHORESCING NOCTILUCA
(naked flagella)

NOCTILUCA REPRODUCING
BY SPORES

SEA URCHIN LARVA 12

SPORE
MAGNIFIED

ACORN BARNACLE LARVA 9

LOBSTER LARVA
13

PARISITIC COLONY
ON COPEPOD

DINOFLAGELLATE

PROTOZOA

PLANKTONIC FORMS OF MARINE LIFE

BACTERIA PHYTOPLANKTON ZOOPLANKTON

BIRD ISLAND

HERRING

COD

HARBOUR SEAL

REDFISH

The feeding grounds

Some environments of the Atlantic coastline provide particularly rich feeding grounds although the nutrients dissolved in the water may come from different sources. Seabirds nesting on a bird island (left) in the Atlantic region add close to 100,000 tons of mineral-rich guano to the water per year, which stimulates enormous plankton growth. Near the edge of any fishing bank (right) currents from offshore waters collide with ocean currents, the turbulence bringing cooler, nutrient-filled water to the surface, attracting swarms of plankton. By trapping the sun's energy and adding oxygen, plant plankton produce a great amount of living matter in the sea. With ample plant food available, animal plankton thrive by the billion. Herring, capelin, squid and shellfish feed on these zooplankton, larger fish such as cod eat smaller fish, and finally the cod are consumed by seals. Through the food cycle, 10,000 pounds of plant plankton are needed to support a one-pound weight gain in a seal. When the seal (or bird, or whale) dies, bacterial action decomposes the body (or plant, or guano) continually making the supply of phosphates and nitrates reusable to the plankton. Thus the cycle of the sea continues.

An underwater view of the Grand Banks shows the vast shelves of rock surrounding Newfoundland.

SEABIRDS

OFFSHORE CURRENT

OCEANIC CURRENT

HERRING

TUNA

HALIBUT

SPERM WHALE

Monsters, myths and other mysteries

Many fierce battles between giant squid and sperm whales have been reported by sailors for centuries, and whales have been caught with great scars about their heads and with fragments of tentacles in their stomachs. Armed with a powerfully sharp beak, and grasping rings of teeth on the sucker discs of its strangling tentacles, the squid can put up a ferocious battle. Squid will even attack sperm whales by swimming alongside, then ahead of the whale, striking just behind the angle of the jaw. Remarkable for their highly developed brains and eyes, squid are also powerful swimmers, ejecting jets of water with immense force to propel themselves backwards. When danger threatens, a squid can effectively camouflage himself by quickly changing colour or squirting out clouds of black ink. The giant squid is the world's largest invertebrate, and nine have been collected in Newfoundland waters, the largest of these being 30 feet long and weighing 300 pounds. Studies by Dr. F. A. Aldrich of Memorial University show squid have the largest nerve fibre in the animal kingdom, but man has not been able to completely penetrate the mysteries and secrets of the elusive squid.

Unlike most molluscs, the squid have separate sexes. During the breeding season an arm of the male swells at the end and fills with sperm-carrying capsules. These are transferred to the female to fertilize her ova (1). The female expels the egg capsules (2) each capsule containing from 20 to 200 eggs (3). The capsules have a sticky end and are attached in bundles to submerged objects. A tough, flexible outer shell protects the eggs from most predators. Inside the cellophane-like egg-shell the embryo develops, feeding on the pear-shaped yolk sac. At this stage the eyes and head are bulky, the mantle and fins less developed. The arms look like sprouts, covered with minute suckers (4). The transparent embryo (5) is a distorted dwarf of the adult just before hatching. After breaking through the egg-shell the tiny squid will briefly become part of the plankton community.

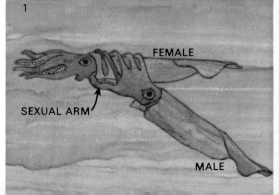

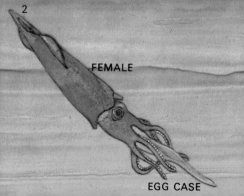

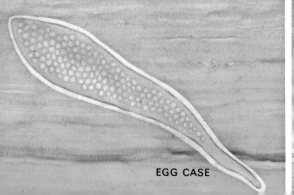

EGG CASE

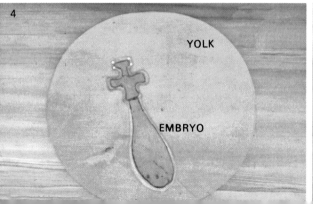

4

YOLK

EMBRYO

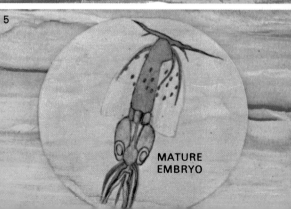

5

MATURE EMBRYO

Bizarre creatures
of the deep

The mysterious inhabitants of the deep sea are only occasionally seen by man. No light reaches the depths of the ocean and many fish are equipped with lighting systems of their own. Because there can be little plant food without light, all deep-sea fish are carnivores, and many of them have large mouths adding to their bizarre appearance. The loosejaw (1) and the longtooth anglemouth (2) are typical deep-sea fish and their bodies and very large mouths are patterned with rows of luminous dots. An almost circular fish, the spinyfin (3) has a highly compressed body and is found in depths up to 2700 fathoms. The black swallower (4), although slender and only twelve inches long, is able to swallow fish many times larger than itself. In order to be able to do this, the black swallower must move its heart out of the way, push its gills to one side, and use teeth located in its throat to push down its prey.

The transparent hatchet fish (5) has several rows of light-organs and is only 1½ inches long. One of the most extraordinary fish is the angler, with its own line and bait (6). The first spine of the dorsal fin is modified into a tentacle with a pear-shaped swelling on the end. When hungry, the angler dangles the lure near its mouth thereby attracting small fish. Another peculiarity of the angler fish is that females grow up to four feet long, whereas the males are no bigger than six inches. The males are parasitic, fastening themselves to a side of the female for most of their lives. No more than a living sperm sac, they are always on hand to fertilize the eggs. The Atlantic batfish (7) and boa dragonfish (8) are restricted to the continental shelf and seldom venture into the deep channels. When a lancetfish (9) is washed ashore, it usually creates quite a stir. This six-foot fish has a long high dorsal fin and a ferocious set of fang-like teeth. It eats everything that crosses its path in the mid-depths and is often an aid to the ichthyologist who must depend on the carnivores for information on rare deep-sea fish. A lancetfish is brought to the surface by long-line fishing, by parasitic infection which drives them out of normal depths, or by ingesting food that acts like a balloon. The snipe eel (10), extremely slender and 3 feet long, has bill-like jaws and recurved teeth.

Blooming in summertime, orchids are found in marshy areas near the Atlantic shores.

PART THREE / **PLANT LIFE**

7 THE COLONIZING PLANTS

Plants are, of course, the original colonists, and they constantly test colonizing possibilities throughout the Atlantic region. Each plant has some special adaptive device which helps it get established where it best can survive. For instance, after a fire, spruce establishes itself before fir because it can get its roots into mineral soil quickly. Fir, on the other hand, can survive for years with its roots solely in the upper layers of humus. After the great Saxby Gale, spruce generally beat the fir to restore the forests wherever the two trees were in competition.

Some plants have extremely specialized development patterns in establishing themselves. After an insect attack has destroyed a forest (notably in the Gaspé in the 1930's, and in New Brunswick in the 1940's), a tremendous growth of raspberries may move throughout the stricken area. For the first four or five years, the plants are giants, five to seven feet high (presumably to choke out all competition), but gradually they grow smaller until after ten years, they are back to their original size. By that time, trees are beginning to make their comeback and eventually subdue the raspberries.

The energy of the regeneration act is a clue to the power of plants to colonize. They may thrust out such enormous numbers of seeds over such distances that every possible habitat, new or existing, is tested. A New Brunswick forest fire among red spruce would likely trigger repopulation with poplar and birch, their light seeds blowing in from miles outside the burn. Poplar seeds are so light they can easily cross miles of open sea to test conditions on offshore islands. They become established very quickly and shade the ground, a discouragement to other trees trying to establish themselves. The seeds of many trees skip for miles across crusted snow.

The scope of regeneration can be seen on almost any forest floor after some break-up has occurred—even a fallen tree. The forest floor immediately sprouts a mat of seedlings of every conceivable variety, millions and millions of plants to the acre. This is the beginning of a rush for the sun, with every plant competing against the next one. Each has a device for beating the other. If balsam fir gets a head start over the other trees, it may begin with millions of seedlings to the acre. These thin themselves to 100,000 after a few years in a process that continues until about 6,000 trees survive in that area.

Although plants blanket the Atlantic region from the highest, rockiest mountains where the environment is nearly Arctic, to many feet down in the sea, most of them fit very precisely into their environments. Silver maple, butternut, and red ash are confined to the lowest part of the St. John River valley and its tributaries, and along the main southwest section of the Miramichi. Hemlock is concentrated in Northumberland County, and it also likes Queens and Lunenburg counties in Nova Scotia. Black cherry thrives between Digby and Yarmouth in Nova Scotia, but not elsewhere. White spruce is fond of abandoned farms, particularly in northern and eastern Nova Scotia.

The eelgrass, a peculiar aquatic plant poised midway between land and sea, and not quite belonging to either, is equally precisely adapted. It colonized the Atlantic region, specifically the southern gulf, through drifting seeds, but it can only survive where there are summer water temperatures between sixty and eighty, and where no heavy storm swells strike. Along the shores of Prince Edward Island, where the eelgrass is thickest, its voluminous, grasping rooting systems trap silt, particularly in estuaries, and thus improve its own habitat.

Most of the plants of the sea are able to colonize, almost instantly, any new environmental opportunity, like the creation of a sea wall or harbour barrier. Their spores are present in all currents and tides, and their uniform distribution, and density of occupation are indications of the success of their colonizing. *Chondrus crispus,* the well-known Irish moss, (an ingredient in ice cream, meringues, cheese, beer) is perhaps the most common sea plant along nearly every mile of the 10,000 miles of shoreline in the Atlantic region.

At its most dense, it creates marine jungles, its yellowish-green, reddish-purple fronds smothering the bottom from the tideline out a mile or so in shallow water. It is particularly heavy in the Northumberland Strait region. All these marine plants, including the tasty dulse (which is dried and eaten as a kind of non-sweet candy by Maritime children), the purple laver, kelp, laminarians, and scores of other seaweeds are constantly sending out spores in search of new rock pools, new gravel beaches, sandy shallows, mudflats and tidal regions to exploit.

Since the retreat of the Pleistocene ice, the plants of the Atlantic region have probably advanced into new colonial areas only to be flung back by intermittently increasing cold, then to advance again, and then retreat, in a process that has been repeated many times. When M. L. Fernald, the American botanist, was in Newfoundland early in the century, he explored the inhospitable Blanc Sablon region, at the Straits of Belle Isle, the area Jacques Cartier had vowed that "God gave to Cain." Fernald, however, found many woodland plants thriving there, apparently survivors of a long-departed forest. On a tableland east of Blanc Sablon, he found buried logs in a bog and many stumps protruding from the moss, about twelve inches in diameter. He assumed that a very large and ancient forest had once fringed the entire length of the straits.

This forest possibly colonized the Blanc Sablon region during the Hypsithermal period, a time when the climate was extremely benign between 9,000 and 5,000 years ago. At this time, it is probable that many plants and animals moved north into areas where they could not possibly colonize today. Newfoundland offers many unique examples of these plant colonizers. Fernald found that most of the typical Canadian plants which, theoretically, should have colonized the islands, were absent. 340 out of 367 species of plants which abound in eastern Canada in the latitudes of Newfoundland never made it to the island. Instead, he found 466 species of boreal types which made up sixty per cent of all the flora of the island, and 216 Arctic alpine species, or thirty per cent of the island's flora.

To complicate this picture, many of the species he found were southern species, occurring as far south as New Jersey. For instance, he found a member of the curly-grass family, the curly-grass fern, in Newfoundland. This is a plant lightly scattered across Nova Scotia, but it is mainly a resident of southern New Jersey. He found broom crowberry, the yellow-eyed grass which occurs from Newfoundland to Pennsylvania, the inkberry which occurs as far south as Florida, and other, isolated members of large, tropical families.

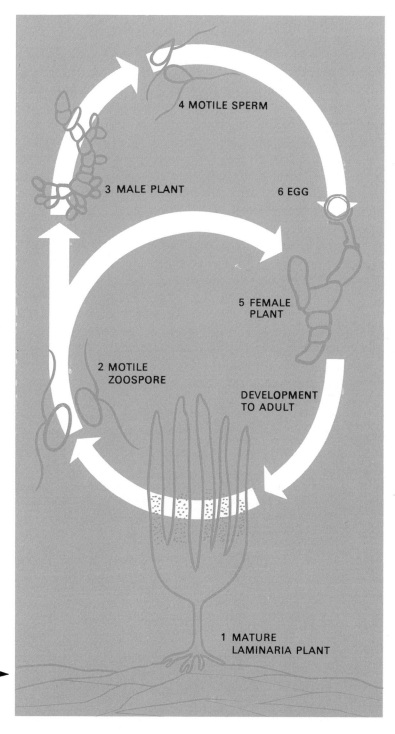

The seaweed Laminaria *has two distinct forms. The mature plant that we usually see (1) gives off motile zoospores (2), forming into microscopic filamentous male (3) or female (5) plants. A male sperm (4) fertilizes a single egg (6) developing it into a mature plant.*

4 MOTILE SPERM

3 MALE PLANT

6 EGG

5 FEMALE PLANT

2 MOTILE ZOOSPORE

DEVELOPMENT TO ADULT

1 MATURE LAMINARIA PLANT

The curly-grass fern, which seeds by spores, is a plant so tiny that it could never hope to do its colonizing work across any large body of water. Even its habitat is peculiar. It is restricted to little hollows in peat bogs which must be sheltered from the wind, and it only grows in August in these potholes, probably until the end of September. Its presence in Newfoundland implies a continuous body of land, stretching from Cape Cod into Newfoundland, along which it could have migrated.

Fernald, in fact, proposed this idea. He said the bridge would have to consist of silicious soils identical to those of the southern New Jersey coastal plain. This would give the migration route to red pines, and to other south-western plants. His theory was ingenious at the time. There is some evidence for a land bridge flanking the eastern coast in immediate post-glacial times, but it must have been widely cut at several points by deep valleys, now drowned, which would have made migration very difficult.

Another explanation for these plant colonists is the Nunatac theory which holds that various high points of Newfoundland, and elsewhere in the Atlantic region, never were glaciated. In these Nunatacs, various plants survived the Pleistocene, and were then able to recolonize Newfoundland while their nearest colleagues were prevented from joining them by hundreds of miles of hostile territory.

The two Nunatacs of the southern Atlantic region seem to support this theory. One is in the Green River region of New Brunswick, near the Quebec border, with a height of about two thousand feet. The other is the highest Cape Breton highland country, at about 2,700 feet. The ecologies of both regions are identical: very large black spruce thrives when it should be growing in boggy land on the lowlands, and there are scattered stems of white birch. The two Nunatacs are three hundred miles apart. The Nunatac theory is also ingenious until examined closely. A 2,700-foot mountain surrounded by glacial ice could never have supported black spruce and white birch anyway.

The Atlantic region abounds with puzzles as to how plant colonizing took place. About one-fifth of the species of plants in Newfoundland is restricted to the west coast which is essentially a limestone region. The limestone-loving yellow birch is common along the coastal strip there, which is understandable. But how did it get to odd outcroppings of limestone country in the east, particularly one at Bay d'Espoir?

Equally puzzling is the placement of the Arctic fleabane which is known to be in two localities in Quebec, one at Baffin Island, one on the west coast of Greenland, and at one place along Newfoundland's Humber River where it grows in a fiord-like region at the end of scree at the top of a slope.

Nearly all these anomalous plants are pioneering species, which makes it even more difficult to tell if they are survivors of the ice or colonizers along migration routes that have since been destroyed. Whatever the explanations, these colonist plants raise doubts about existing hypotheses concerning the extent and nature of the glacial period.

The Nunatac theory states that certain high peaks in the Green River region (1), the Cape Breton highlands (2) and Newfoundland (3) were not covered by glaciers at any time. The isolated occurrences and strange colonizing patterns of plants are factors which gave rise to this theory.

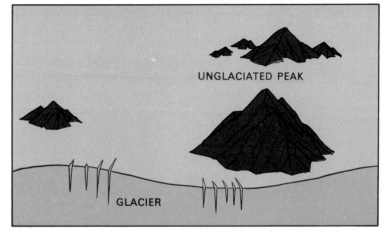

UNGLACIATED PEAK

GLACIER

8 THE DYNAMIC FOREST

When Jacques Cartier sailed along the Atlantic shores in the early 16th century, he rhapsodized over the mighty forests. Explorers and travellers who followed him over the centuries echoed his feelings, particularly at the white pines, some nearly two hundred feet high. Down to the present day has endured a legend of tall and stately forests, dominated by giant trees, which covered the entire Atlantic region. The true facts are, however, somewhat different.

Cartier *did* see mighty trees, especially large white pines. What he did not see (due to his preference for the ship's deck rather than the uncertainties of primeval dry land) was that behind the white pines were forests of spruce, and balsam fir, beech, maple, birch, hemlock and others; the same sort of forests that presently cover the Atlantic shore region.

Another myth, created in the very recent past of the 20th century, is that the Maritime forests have suffered unique new disasters at the hands of man as a result of his restless search for lumber, paper pulp, ships' masts, shingles, and other items. In fact, as foresters now well know, the worst catastrophes in the Atlantic forests have nothing to do with man. They are administered by weather and insects, which are constant, unchangeable forces at work modifying the mix of life of the forests.

The Saxby Gale of 1869 smashed several thousand square miles of forest. Even today, it is possible to walk through New Brunswick forests and see the bodies of fallen victims of the Saxby, rotten on the outside but still containing thousands of feet of millable lumber on the inside. In places, the forest floor is pock-marked, as though by saturation bombing, forty to fifty craters to the acre, with holes left by trees uprooted during that great storm.

In the early 17th century, Father Chretien LeClerq, a Jesuit priest, saw the entire Miramichi watershed aflame—a fire caused by Indians or lightning—and his description of the fire was given a horrifying, 19th century sequel when, in the dry summer of 1826, about 6,000 square miles of the Miramichi and other forest regions burned, killing more than five hundred people. The fire destroyed the lumbering industry in the area and put the city of Newcastle into a decline from which it is still struggling to recover. Botanists estimate that at least fifty percent of Nova Scotia has burned at least once in the last two hundred years.

Insect attacks, dreaded by modern man with his heavy investment in and dependance on healthy tree growth, are as old as the forests themselves and, in fact, were often necessary to healthy succession in primeval forests. The spruce budworm attack beginning in 1912 in the forests of central New Brunswick caused regeneration of the commercially profitable modern forests.

The extent of the three "disasters" was so great that a forester once claimed that every forest in the province could be precisely dated by the residual marks of the Saxby, the Miramichi blaze, and the budworm attack. Violent change in forests is, therefore, normal.

The dynamic nature of forest process is indicated by the scope and mix of the various Atlantic forests. The most abundant tree is the fragrant balsam fir. Growing singly, it is a dense, triangular-shaped, bushy tree. Its method of generation is through sheer numbers. After a tree falls in the forest, the forest floor is a mat of sprouting seedlings of every conceivable variety, millions upon millions of plants to the acre. But it is the balsam fir which will win, its densely-massed seedlings eliminating all competition. As they grow, they eliminate their weaker selves to about five thousand trees per acre.

The balsam fir can grow almost anywhere in the Atlantic region, from rock-strewn mountains to near-boglands. It has pushed its way throughout inhospitable Newfoundland to densely populate every habitat where the soil is deep enough (about twelve inches) to accommodate its roots. As a young tree, it can survive almost indefinitely in the deep shade, waiting for that opportunity when a break occurs in the canopy, when the sun comes streaming down and it can begin its race for the sun and maturity which may come one hundred and fifty years later.

The red spruce, which rivals the balsam fir in numbers and may exceed it in range of territory, is adapted to take advantage of catastrophes. It gets away rapidly after hurricane destruction. If, as a seedling, it can get its roots into mineral soil, it will beat out everything after a fire. However, it is much more likely that the tiny seeds of poplar and birch, blowing like thistledown for hundreds of miles, will reach into the burn area first, establish a kind of nursery crop for twenty years, time enough for the ubiquitous red spruce to come in beneath this crop, and thus eventually end up as the dominant tree.

The dynamics of the Atlantic forests can be measured in an idealized picture. If the 100,000-odd square miles of forests in the shore region were growing in a uniform, flat, well-drained, fertile, moderately wintered environment and consisted of various mixes of spruces, firs, oaks, maples, and others, the region would contain about seven billion trees. About an equal number of seedling trees would be pushing up beneath them. Among the seedlings would be about thirty billion shrubs and about three thousand billion herbaceous plants.

In this ideal forest, about 770 million pairs of small birds

would live, split into their specialist ranges. In the brush-forest country, towhees, field sparrows and Nashville and chestnut-sided warblers would live. In young forest regions (recovering from fires or gale destruction) ovenbirds, redstarts, red-eyed vireos and ruffed grouse would hunt. The evergreen fir, spruce and pine forests would hold warblers—Blackburnians, black-throateds and magnolias—and olive-backed thrushes.

In such forests—especially in an old forest of maple-beech-hemlock as might be found in primeval New Brunswick—ninety per cent of the ground would be shaded from direct sunlight. Warblers would teem in the canopy in search of invertebrates, especially spiders. At the height of the summer, several thousand insects would occupy every thirty square feet of the canopy and even greater numbers would live in the ground levels.

This one-hundred-thousand-square-mile region, thus ideal-

ized, would hold several thousand mountain lions and wolves, 300,000 foxes, 50,000 black bears, about two billion mice, and several million assorted mammals, such as raccoons, skunks, woodchucks, squirrels and others. In fact, of course, nothing like this ideal exists anywhere in the Atlantic region. The area is too broken up by river valleys, by the effects of fires, or geological intrusions, by thin acid or boggy soils, by the influence of winds and excessive rain, and by the proximity of the sea.

Newfoundland, so harshly hit by the glacial period, is testimony to this. Only about forty per cent of it is forested; the rest of the land is covered with large and small lakes, ponds, sedge bogs, great areas of sub-alpine tundra, barrens caused by fires, and scrubland. The non-forested regions are vivid visual reminders not only of the paucity of the soil, often only half an inch thick, but of the very recentness of the retreat of the ice.

Endless vistas of barrens and boglands on which grow mosses, lichens and some stunted pioneering trees, flowering plants, and grasses, are seen everywhere.

All the forests, which are thickest and most successful in the many rivers and valleys of the island, are dominated by some combination of balsam fir, black spruce, white spruce, and white birch. The red spruce, with its large seeds and its fondness for lowland loams, never made it. Nearly all the island's trees, except those in the most sheltered valleys, fall eventually in the grip of the wind. The soils, of glacial origin, so thinly cover the sedimentary bedrock that it does not give much chance for tree roots to get a grip and withstand wind.

A balsam fir, or a white spruce, growing in four to six inches of sandy loam covering pure bedrock, can reach fifty feet in a hundred years with a trunk diameter of twelve inches. A

Delicate blossoms

This dragon's mouth (1) was found growing in a bog at Bonne Bay, Newfoundland. A fairly rare orchid, it is a perennial growing from a single bulb. Orchids generally grow slowly, are hard to transplant, and have minute seeds.

Orchids are the largest family of flowering plants with up to 20,000 species, most of them tropical. The moccasin flower (2) like so many orchids, likes acid, poor soil and depends on fungi surrounding the roots for at least part of its food.

This fragrant early spring flower is the provincial flower of Nova Scotia. Trailing arbutus (3) is a creeping evergreen shrub which grows in rocky acid soil, with leathery, hairy leaves helping to conserve precious moisture.

white birch grows about half that rate in the same conditions, reaching forty-five feet in 180 years. Eventually, however, as all these trees reach maturity, it is the wind that knocks them down and the process begins again with the mass of seedlings reaching hopefully from that thin soil.

However, none of this is to suggest that Newfoundland is a botanical wilderness. On the contrary, every peak and valley, every barren and bog, reveals the relentless attempts by plant life to reach into every available habitable place. In the high barrens, where the soil might be as thin as an inch over bedrock, black spruce sprouts, spreads its roots wide and crouches down close against the ground to form, as one botanist put it, "a dense prostrate shrub layer." When the soil gets thinner than two inches, the black spruce cannot make it but is replaced by a dense mat of plants, especially the blueberry. The sedge bogs, which can be either in valleys or in barren uplands, are also packed with plants, including orchids.

All this is part of the immensely slow process of recovering the land from the age of ice, of building up the soil, breaking up the rocks, and increasing the productivity of the environment. Unfortunately, this process was interrupted several thousand years too soon by man. This is nowhere better illustrated than by the role that fire has played in Newfoundland, and elsewhere in the Atlantic region, since the arrival of Caucasian man.

The Miramichi fire, now nearly a century and a half distant, is today merely a mark in the trunks of the oldest trees, but in Newfoundland no such rapid recovery from fire is ever possible. When, in the early 1960's, thousands of acres burned during one of the hottest and driest summers on record, the flames did more than menace towns and villages, destroy farms, livestock and lumber stocks. Some, caught by sea winds, roared like freight trains through thick spruce and balsam fir growth, and their passage was so fast that not a single tree was killed. Others, working on calm days, burned slowly at ground level, destroyed up to two feet of accumulated organic matter in the soil until the trees toppled into the burning debris and so were roasted. Along the east coast of the island, the fires burned so fiercely foresters predicted that little or no tree growth was likely there for one, and possibly two, human generations.

The fires illuminated the island's history since white men arrived. Repeated fires, as few as three every century, are suf-ficient to transform entire areas into what are known locally as "goodwiddy" or "goldwithy," a dwarf growth consisting largely of laurels, Labrador tea, and blueberries. Much, or all, of the Avalon peninsula was probably forested before Cabot sighted Newfoundland in the early 16th century but now, after four hundred years of flame, it is almost entirely barrenlands.

Elsewhere on the Atlantic shoreline, fire plays quite a different role when it strikes into more benign environments. There, it can be seen as a normal part of forest succession. A forest endures for perhaps three hundred years, surmounted by giant red spruces which, one by one, begin to fall. The forest floor is littered with the debris of 10,000 days of changing seasons. Growth is very slow and bird and mammal life is low. Then, inevitably, fire strikes. It was as likely started by a Micmac Indian, tired of trying to hunt in such dense growth, as by any other method.

In the ensuing burn can be seen the various adaptations that the different trees have made to fire. The black spruce, that tough colonizer of thin soils, soggy pits and bogs (some New Brunswick bogs have grown black spruce uninterruptedly for 5,000 years) forms cones at the top of its stem which do not open like the ones lower down. Instead, they accumulate year after year, for perhaps as long as twenty years. Then comes fire; the heat bursts open the cones and the seeds flutter down. The jackpine is equally fire-born. It needs 110 degrees of heat to open its seed cones and its colonizing of large lowland areas along the coast of New Brunswick is almost certain indication of a big fire, or fires, there sometime in the past.

The adaptation of jackpine and black spruce to fire is in contrast to the vulnerability of balsam fir to it. Its life force has evolved to seize almost every opportunity except that provided by fire. Fire wipes it out and it can only repopulate a burned area from the outside.

The birches have no defences against fire either. But if there is a race to repopulate a burned area, the birch will beat the balsam fir. Its tiny seeds, equipped with fine wings, are wind-borne and once the seedlings get a hold it may be a century or more

The path of a disastrous fire can be seen in the desolation of Wreck ▶
Cove, Cape Breton; unharmed vegetation thrives in the foreground.

before the balsam fir, patiently waiting in the wings, as it were, gets its chance to invade. However, the birch does not necessarily form a stable forest. It grows too fast for its own good and chokes out its own regeneration. This ensures a later triumph for the spruces or the firs, and the continued cycling of succession.

Into this complex process we may now inject the work of man and insects. The first exploitation of the Maritime forests was likely the cutting of spars for, first, the French navy, and then for the British navy which did as much as anything else to wipe out all the big white pines. The French man o' war, *Avenant*, was freighting pine masts out of the St. John River as early as 1700. Nova Scotia was stripped of its mast material in the 1760's and New Brunswick forests suffered heavily during the American revolution and the Napoleonic wars when a 90-foot stem, 35 inches in diameter, sold in Saint John for an incredible $450.

This eliminated all the tall straight trees. Then came heavy demand for square timber, called ton-wood, mainly smaller pine with some birch and other hardwoods also being sought. This exploitation remained fairly constant until the 1830's when the "heroic age of logging began," as one historian has put it, a period that led sensibly to the great shipbuilding days, demanding immense quantities of sawn wood. In those years, all the millable coastal trees were eliminated. A Nova Scotian might need to walk up to twenty miles inland to reach a stand of trees he could cut and saw. White pine was in such demand that by the 1830's and '40's, it was scarce throughout the Atlantic region. By 1860, sixty per cent of all the wood cut in New Brunswick was spruce.

Shipbuilding demanded a diversified cut. Pine and red spruce were used for spars, larch for underwater planking, stanchions, ship's knees, beams, and tree nails, black and yellow birch being favoured immediately after larch. The exploitation of the forests resulted in smaller and smaller trees (a fact that was duplicated in the sea by the catching of smaller and smaller fish). In the 18th century a grove of white pines could yield more than twenty thousand board feet of lumber. In 1830, it took three logs to yield one thousand feet of lumber, in 1881, nine logs, and in 1904, seventeen logs. Today, five thousand board feet of lumber to the acre is considered good cutting.

Then, in the 1920's and '30's, the pulp and paper mills began working, particularly in Newfoundland (where a few powerful interests got complete control of almost the entire forestland of the island), ushering in an era of exploiting the softwoods which, before that time, were left undisturbed.

Human exploitation became a geographical force. The tank-bark industry destroyed all the hemlock in southern New Brunswick. The heavy cutting of spruce boosted the regeneration of balsam fir which, in turn, set the scene for the subsequent spruce bud-worm plagues. The cutting of spruce and balsam fir created succeeding stands of birch, red maple and aspen. The demand for shingles and poles slashed cedar numbers everywhere. Demand for red oak made that tree scarce by the middle of the 19th century.

The chestnut blight eliminated all the southern New Brunswick chestnuts (the tree was at the limit of its northern range there) by the end of the 19th century. At the same time, the larch sawfly obliterated nearly all mature larch throughout the Atlantic region. Recently, larch seems to be attempting a hesitating comeback.

The beech bark disease, which got into New Brunswick in 1890, has destroyed almost all the mature beech in the southern part of the province and throughout Nova Scotia, resulting in radical changes in many forests where the beech was dominant. In place of the beech, red spruce, fir, and sugar maple have moved into the area.

The balsam woolly aphid, introduced from Europe, is breaking up balsam fir stands, in the southern Atlantic region. Birch dieback, a baffling killer (it might be caused by slightly lowered ground temperatures or by a virus) has destroyed most of the mature yellow and white birch in the Atlantic region since 1940. The birches are fighting back and since 1948 have been reproducing in what were once disaster areas. A blister rust has worked its way through most of the white pine stands and is now searching out the few remaining stands of the pines in Newfoundland.

Despite all this destruction, Atlantic shore forest life is dynamic, a major wealth-producer and, at this moment, an expanding crop which is taking over thousands of abandoned or uneconomic farms where men have finally conceded that the land is meant to grow trees, not corn.

ON THE EDGE OF THE OCEAN

The Atlantic coastline provides many varied habitats for its wildlife—the sandy beaches of Prince Edward and Sable Islands, the rocky shorelines of Newfoundland and the Gaspé, and the great expanse of tidal flats of the Bay of Fundy and Minas Basin. Above, a greater yellowlegs seeks a meal among the shallows.

Along a sandy beach

Although many plants and animals inhabit sandy beaches, it is a precarious home, constantly changed by the action of waves, wind, currents and storms. Strong winds can uproot plants, and as plant roots are vital to holding sand in one place, whole dunes can change position in a short time. Sandy Sable Island is literally held together by plant roots. Storms in the Maritimes can sweep away the top surface of sand, exposing burrowing animals to the sun and air. Dry upper parts of sandy beaches are sparse in animal life, but the moisture-soaked surf line abounds with digging molluscs, crabs, sand hoppers and beach-fleas. One of the most stable environments of sandy shorelines is the microscopic world in between the sand grains, where for any given volume of sand, one-fifth will be air. Here, hidden to the eye, tiny plants surface at low tide for photosynthesis, and tiny animals feed at high tide.

A shore scene at Western Brook, Newfoundland, with dead trees polished by wind and sand.

This greatly-enlarged photograph shows ▶ a beach hopper burrowing into the sand.

The senecio has stout, fibrous roots to anchor it in the shifting sand.

Semipalmated plovers flock to the seashores in the summer, probing the sand for intertidal animals.

The horsehoe crab will come ashore only to build a nest in the sand and breed.

Sea plantain thrives in crevices of rocks, varying widely in height, size of leaves, and length of life.

On a rocky shore

Long stretches of rocky shores are common along the Atlantic coast, but despite the force of the tide, this environment is more stable than that of the sandy shores. Rich concentrations of animal and plant life fill the tidal pools in rock crevices — scuttling crabs, starfish of many different colours, clustered colonies of sea anemones, flowerlike hydroids, iridescent Irish moss, red dulse and fronds of brown kelp. These life forms cannot stand much exposure to air. Higher up, the cliffs are covered with rockweed and a host of different molluscs, blue mussels, periwinkles and sea-snails. At the highest range of the tide are the barnacles and acorn-snails. Above the high tide mark, green algae known as sea hair can live on the moisture thrown by waves against the rocks. Above this level, the hardy lichens thrive, often enduring long periods with no moisture.

The lower rocks of this coastline in Newfoundland are marked with coloured bands of intertidal life.

The sun star, which has from 8 to 14 arms, prowls along the rocky shore for molluscs, other echinoderms and sea anemones.

Bottom right:
At low tide, different plant and animal zones are clearly visible on the rocky shore from low to high water marks.

The Atlantic salmon exploits the sea from the surface to the depths, voraciously feeding on favourite fish and many crustaceans.

Between the tides

To survive in the intertidal region where they are scoured by rushing tides and changing water levels, animals and plants must cling to the rocks or burrow in the sand. To help them resist the force of the tide, barnacles secrete limey plates to permanently attach their shells to the rocks; limpets cling by suction valves; scallops have silken fibres and pneumatic discs to bind them to other shells, and algae use their strongly-developed holdfasts. The animals have had to make several adaptations in order to cope with the fluctuating water levels. When exposed to air, a barnacle closes the valve at the top of its shell, making a snug chamber, and the seawater inside helps to aerate its blood until the next high tide. Ability to withstand exposure governs how high the tidal zone periwinkles climb.

◄ *The unusual mouth of the sea urchin has five jaws joined together to form an intricate, highly effective scraping mechanism for food.*

► *Hermit crabs borrow an empty mollusc shell for a home, retreating inside when attacked. While growing, they often change homes.*

Periwinkles change position as the tides vary with the lunar cycle.

The feathery legs of the barnacle sweep plankton from the water.

This small clown jellyfish attaches itself to rocks. The large reddish structures are reproductive organs.

PART FOUR / ANIMAL LIFE

9 THE COLONIZING ANIMALS

The animals of the Maritimes are all, in a sense, creatures of the sea. They live so close to it, and many, in previous millenia, migrated from the mainland to colonize offshore islands. This colonizing process, deliberate, involuntary, accidental, never stops. When a polar bear stepped off an ice floe in the 1880's and landed on Sturge's Island off the east coast of Newfoundland, it was following an ancient habit of deliberate migration. Bears rode the ice pans to drop off anywhere along the Newfoundland coast that caught their fancy. Arctic foxes did likewise, but hunting pressure by men in the north has long since ended this movement of bears and foxes.

When Jacques Cartier landed on Funk Island in 1534, he saw a polar bear "as great as any cow and as white as any swan." The bear plunged into the sea and headed for land about thirty miles away but Cartier's crew overtook it and shot it. The days of voluntary colonizing in which small changes in local environments were constantly tested by the travelling mammals were in jeopardy the moment Caucasian man arrived in the Atlantic region.

Almost all creatures tend to reproduce rapidly and create pressure on the existing limits of the area in which they live, and in the Atlantic region, this can be observed both at short range (the recent arrival and departure of a crab in the region) and at long range (the colonizing of the area after the withdrawal of the Pleistocene ice).

The capacity of life to travel, to fill holes in environments was well demonstrated after the destruction of Krakatoa in August, 1883. The island was about twelve miles from the nearest land mass. Ferns and flowering plants took three years to recolonize the island. Spiders, flies, bugs, beetles, butterflies, moths and lizards made it in six years. At the twenty-five-year mark, there were 263 species of animals on the island, including sixteen bird and two reptile.

The Atlantic region has some colonist populations which are direct evidence of geological and climatological events since the end of the ice age. An oyster drill (a snail which attacks shellfish) has no larval drift and has to walk wherever it goes.

Today, it lives in the southern gulf region, yet it could not have migrated into the gulf around chilly Cape Breton. It is likely that the drill got into the gulf when the *Chignecto Isthmus*, separating Nova Scotia from New Brunswick, was still submerged after the depression under the ice. The land rose, the channel into the gulf disappeared, and the colonizing was over. Some of the drills were stranded in the Bay of Fundy. There, the old oyster populations did not survive, but the drills eat barnacles which seem to suit them well enough.

More recently, the rise and fall of the green crab is a spectacular example of a creature colonizing a new habitat, and then being flung out of it by a minor change in the environment. The first crab was found in the Atlantic region in 1951, near St. Andrews, New Brunswick, in the Bay of Fundy. Several crabs were found in 1952; they were abundant in 1953, and near to being a plague by 1954, with gulls gorging themselves on them everywhere, and raccoons scuttling out onto the tidal flats in daylight to turn over the stones in search of the crabs. But in 1955, the water temperature went down one degree, and within a few years, the crab had disappeared.

The colonizing process, mostly effected in the thousands of years since the withdrawal of the Wisconsin ice, is partially visible to us today. During the withdrawal of the ice sheet, many factors were at work which contributed to the placement of mammals. It is easy to understand that Cape Breton Island and Prince Edward Island have only slightly fewer native species than Nova Scotia and New Brunswick. Colonizing those two islands involved short, over-the-sea migrations on early spring ice, presenting few problems.

But Newfoundland, Anticosti and the Magdalen Islands are another matter. They have fifty per cent fewer species than the mainland areas. Among the animals which never made the migration are starnose moles, shorttailed shrews, pygmy shrews, water shrews, saddle-backed shrews, smoky cinereous shrews, snowshoe hares, woodchucks, chipmunks, red squirrels, flying squirrels, wood mice, bog lemmings, red-backed mice, meadow-jumping mice, woodland-jumping mice, and porcupines.

The wolf got to Newfoundland but he was eliminated from the island in the 19th century. He never made it to Prince Edward Island or Cape Breton. The raccoon, curiously, never made it to any of the islands, and neither did the striped skunk.

The bobcat reached Cape Breton; the caribou got to Newfoundland but not to Anticosti or the Magdalens. The Arctic hare reached Newfoundland but did not colonize the peninsula of Nova Scotia.

The earliest migrants, the wolf, the fox, the black bear, the marten, the otter and the lynx, have been colonizers long enough to undergo evolutionary changes in their skull structures and pelagic colors.

Colonizing Sable Island, that speck of sand so far offshore, would seem to be beyond the capacity of any creature except birds and aquatic mammals. Its unique animal is the Ipswich sparrow, a descendant of a few pairs of savannah sparrows which colonized Sable Island hundreds or thousands of years ago. The island early became famous for its man-introduced colonists. Sir Humphrey Gilbert, writing of his 1583 visit to Newfoundland in the *Golden Hind*, noted that "the Portugals above thirty years past did put into the island neat (cattle) and swine . . . which were since then exceedingly multiplied."

For three hundred years, domestic animals have escaped from Sable shipwrecks while their masters drowned, and the island was always being stocked with some sort of new animal. To the disgust of Sable visitors, domestic pigs gone wild ate everything washed ashore, dying or dead, animal or human. It is horses, however, which have the most durable fame on Sable. They have probably been on the island since the 16th century, escapees from settlers' wrecks. In hard times, their population has been as low as 150, and in lush times, as high as five hundred. One Sable Islander, Captain J. A. Farquhar, said there were about four hundred horses in the mid-19th century. "I learned to ride when I was eight," he wrote, "and had many exciting chases after them, occasionally lassooing one, which would be broken in for general use."

The waves of migrants into Sable created a flux of wildlife, not without its humour for the human observer. The first rabbits reached the island early in the 19th century. Rabbitlike, they multiplied. Farquhar's Newfoundland dog became hysterical at

After the glaciers retreated, animals slowly recolonized the Maritimes. Islands close to the mainland, such as P.E.I., have slightly fewer types (no wolves, raccoons, or skunks). Only half the species on the mainland made it as far as Newfoundland, Anticosti and the Magdalen Islands.

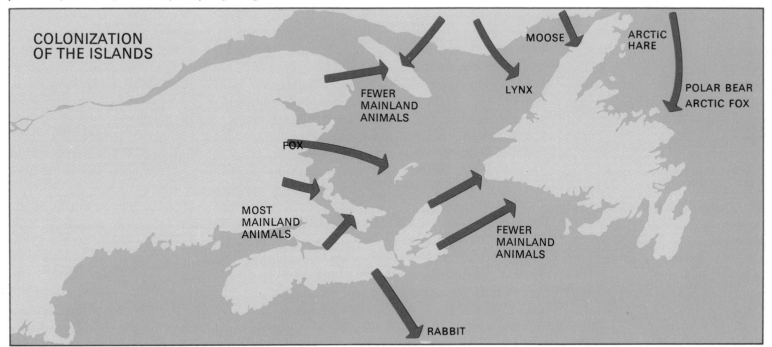

COLONIZATION
OF THE ISLANDS

FEWER
MAINLAND
ANIMALS

MOOSE

ARCTIC
HARE

LYNX

POLAR BEAR
ARCTIC FOX

FOX

MOST
MAINLAND
ANIMALS

FEWER
MAINLAND
ANIMALS

RABBIT

the ease of hunting, although a lone dog could scarcely dent the rabbit host. The proliferation of rabbits coincided with a plague of rats. At one time, the two populations became so troublesome that the islanders decided to control them. They imported cats. The cats killed most of the rats and then decimated the rabbits. But the cats became so numerous and wild that dogs were imported to hunt them. The dogs and the shotguns wiped out the cats but by this time, the rabbits were ascendant again. A snowy owl, chancing on the island, found a hunting paradise. Within a few years, the island was overrun by snowy owls. The rabbit population crashed. The owls, presumably, flew back to the mainland and left the island to the returning rats.

The island is a resting place for migrants and before the great hunting days of the Maritimes decimated the birds it was often smothered with migrating curlew, plover, bluewing teal and snipe. Thousands of seals whelped on its beaches. Occasionally, walrus bones and tusks are washed up out of the sand to show that Sable likely was a breeding ground in the deep past. It is no surprise that walrus are extinct in the area, but less comprehensible is a report by a Bostonian, John Rose, in the 17th century, that the island simultaneously was overrun by foxes and a large herd of cattle. The cattle are easy to account for, perhaps they were an attempt by an anonymous farmer to exploit the grass of the island, but where did foxes come from, on an island one hundred miles out to sea?

Since the original colonizing of the Maritime islands, the regional ecologies have been adjusting to man-made colonizings with sometimes odd results. The snowshoe hare was introduced into Newfoundland some time in the early 19th century by man, and population explosions occurred in 1898, 1914, 1935, 1937, 1951 and 1953. Hunters and trappers frequently got two hundred animals in a couple of nights' work. (A Stephenville Crossing hunter, Joe Walls, killed eighty-seven rabbits with a .22 rifle one afternoon in 1938 near Lake Ambrose.) But the introduction and spread of the snowshoe hare had a profound effect on the lives of the local lynx. Although the lynx reached the island thousands of years before, it never built up populations as big as those of the mainland. Its chief mainland prey, the snowshoe hare, was missing. The lynx hunted the Arctic hare on the island, and kept its numbers down. As a local adaptation

system, the lynx turned its attention to caribou and developed a system, hunting in pairs, of cutting a small or sick animal out of a herd. The male lynx attacked the head, blinding the animal, while the female went for the other vital regions.

Then came the snowshoe hare, fecund, fleet, and able to thrive almost everywhere on the island. A lynx can eat 127 snowshoe hares a year, and if enough snowshoes are available, a pair of lynx will increase to twenty-five in five years, assuming no mortality. Throughout the range of the snowshoe hare, the lynx proliferated. By 1953, the lynx were so thick in western Newfoundland that local farmers set out after them. In three years they killed 315 lynx, one animal for every two square miles of the area.

The starling, which was imported into the United States from Europe in the 19th century, arrived in Newfoundland around 1943. It established small local colonies on the west coast of the island and by 1956, had spread over much of the entire island. In the winter of 1956-57, the starlings created their first major upset of local ecology. Robin populations had found it possible to overwinter in the city of St. John's, sustained in part by the abundance of mountain ash there. But in 1956-57, the berry crop failed. This might not have proved fatal to the robins except that with starlings in the area, they were forced to compete for what little food remained. The starlings won. By late January of 1957, the last of the robins had disappeared.

In colonizing the islands, the animals made adaptations, such as caribou-hunting lynx, to survive or best fit into new environments. There are, according to evolutionary theory, three kinds of adaptations—structural, physiological and behavioral. The exciting thing about the Maritimes is that at least one of these evolutionary adaptations, behavioral, can be seen in process as creatures colonize new areas.

Kent Island, a speck of land in the Bay of Fundy off the large island of Grand Manan, was colonized by muskrats early in this century. It is likely they swam to Kent Island because they have been seen swimming ten miles farther offshore from Kent. But however they got there, they almost immediately began making a strange adaptation to their new environment.

Because there are no predators on Kent Island, and because there are no streams or ponds where the muskrats might build their characteristic aquatic lodges, they dug long, meandering

In a clever behavioural adaptation to man's presence, gulls follow a fishing boat out to sea to eat the offal provided when the fish catch is gutted.

tunnels through the soft soil under the island's colonies of ducks and gulls. On nearby Hay Island, accessible at low tide over intervening mud flats, they did not even bother to dig burrows, but pushed tunnels through the thick grass and undergrowth.

The willow ptarmigans of Newfoundland, introduced to the island as a game bird in the 1920's, offered little sport to local hunters. They skulked, and ran into underbush or long grass instead of flushing. But after a decade or so of chivvying, the ptarmigan has adapted. Now, it is nervous and quick to flush.

Gulls have made many ingenious behavioral adaptations to man's presence. They use coastal ferries to reach offshore islands without the effort of flying. They follow men walking through or near other seabird colonies and seize eggs and nestlings when parent birds are frightened from their nests. They know when fishing boats gut the fish catch at sea, thus providing

offal for them, and they follow the boats out to sea. They do not follow boat crews who gut on shore.

On Kent Island, harried for generations by egg-loving Grand Mananers, the gulls took to nesting in trees, probably in the 18th century. When John James Audubon reached the island, he was astonished to see gulls perching in trees, a most unusual habit for them. Today, with the egg-hunters and plumage-seekers gone, the gulls have de-adapted. They no longer nest in trees but they still perch on branches. If these gulls were isolated from mainland gulls for a few thousand years, physiological adaptations to their feet would occur.

Like all the animals which have colonized new territories, they are feeling the pressure of their environment which stimulates the adaptive process. On this fact is based the success or failure of all life in the Atlantic region.

10 TEEMING PLANKTON ARMIES

The plankton teem in the seas of the Atlantic region, up to twenty million of them in a cubic foot of water. As microscopic plants and animals, they stand at the beginning of all marine life systems. They are the bottom layer in what ecologists call "the pyramid of numbers." The plants, or phytoplankton, the simplest form of life, perform the simplest function; they trap the sun's energy through photosynthesis, and are eaten by the next layer in the pyramid, the animals, or zooplankton.

Each step upward in the pyramid sees a ten-to-one loss in material bulk. A ton of phytoplankton produces only two hundred pounds of zooplankton, which support ten pounds of small fish flesh, which produce one pound of large fish flesh, which cause 1.6 ounces of flesh gain in a man eating one pound of fish flesh.

The plankton swarm, they are eaten, they die, they sink to the bottom where they feed clams and tube worms and bacteria. Their bodies are converted into fertilizing chemicals which are carried to the surface to begin the process over. In past millenia, they have formed geological structures through the sheer density of their numbers.

The diatoms stand at the beginning of the planktonic life process. These plants of the sea, viewed up close, glisten like sparks of fire and colour the sea green. Each plant is an individual cell which in times of growing populations divides again and again.

Upon the success of this division is hinged the fertility of the sea. Diatoms go through two population upsurges a year; one in the spring that lasts into summer, and the other in the fall. They proliferate only when they have ample sunlight and an abundance of nitrates and phosphates.

During the winter, phosphates and nitrates accumulate from the decay of plant and animal materials. These are available in the spring when the diatoms awake from overwintering spores, surrounded by walls of silica, and rise to prey on the chemicals.

The diatoms feed the two other main types of planktonic life at the surface—the permanent and the temporary. The permanent plankton are billions of tiny crustacea which live constantly at the surface. The temporary are the countless larvae of shore and marine animals which go through a drift period before settling into adult life.

Scarcely less numerous than the phytoplankton are the zooplankton which include the incredibly abundant copepods, each about the size of the head of a pin. They are offshore-breeding, single-generation animals which, at the height of their numbers, might be the most abundant creature in the sea, or on earth, their populations extending for hundreds of miles across the open sea.

Another group of extremely abundant offshore planktonic creatures in the Atlantic region are the euphausids, tiny shrimp-like crustaceans that are a favorite whale food and which, in Arctic waters, are dubbed *krill*, and are scooped up by the blue, the fin and the humpback whale by the ton.

Other single-celled organisms in the plankton are the dino-flagellates which exist on the borderline between animal and plant. They are single-celled but slightly larger than diatoms, and they can propel themselves through the water with two whip-like flagella. Some are phosphorescent and flash lights visible at night. Given ideal conditions with no mortality, a pair of them could smother the earth with their progeny in eleven days.

The observer looks at this teeming planktonic life through a microscope and, if he is seeing it for the first time, is puzzled by the seemingly infinite variety of shapes—squares, tubes, geometric designs. They are, as a marine biologist put it recently, "an assemblage of creatures more diverse than anything else on earth."

In indescribable variety they drift and float. Some are fish eggs buoyed up on a single drop of oil; others are larvae of fish sustained by a yolk sac or spreading hairs which make them float like thistledown.

Within the plankton there is constant war. Tiny arrow-worms eat the fish larvae; larvae eat other larvae or eggs—or their own kind. Bacteria are omnipresent. They teem at the surface and thrive in the deeps. They feed on any organic matter and so produce the carbon dioxide, the phosphates and the nitrates necessary for the other lives.

The planktonic hordes are not helpless victims of their environment. They rise and fall, taking advantage of submarine currents, to move around in the sea or to save themselves from death. The Lusitanian plankton of the eastern Atlantic can drop down 3,600 feet and travel hundreds of miles before being welled to the suface.

The up-and-down movements of the zooplankton express one of the many rhythmic cycles of life in the Atlantic region. They are responding, it is believed, to varying intensities of light. When the light is bright, they theoretically become more responsive to gravity and sink until the light becomes dim. Their response to gravity diminishes in proportion and so they stop. Then, as the sun sinks in the late afternoon, the process is reversed. Gravity response diminishes and they rise to the surface. Awaiting them are the teeming hordes of plant plankton which have spent the day proliferating under the light of the sun. The purpose of this up and down movement is not precisely known but it certainly keeps the zooplankton away from the many creatures which hunt plant plankton on the surface. It also enables them to move from place to place during the night hours when surface currents transport them.

A Newfoundland marine biologist once was intrigued by the fate of zooplankton at the coast during storms. Were they driven ashore to die en masse? During a violent storm on the west coast, he combed the shallow waves but did not find a single zooplankton animal. After the storm, he recovered thousands of them. These tiny creatures apparently could detect the onset of a storm and drop to the bottom until it was over.

The biology of the plankton is never simple. The male of the pinhead-sized copepoda manufactures a tubular-necked "bottle" into which it squirts its sperm. Then it swims in search of a female. The "bottle" is attached to her abdomen by a pair of the male's thoracic limbs. From the "bottle" the sperm passes into a storage cavity in the female's body. When she lays her single eggs, they are fertilized as they pass through this cavity.

There are constant adjustments of plankton populations as the Maritime plankton go through cycles of upsurge and downfall. The arrow-worms have lived in the plankton hordes, in one form or another, for perhaps 500 million years. They are present in Cambrian fossil evidence. Transparent, almost invisible except for two tiny black eyes, the worm can fire itself six times its own length with a lash of its whip-like tail. It seizes a larval herring or a diatom with a cluster of bristles at its head and the victim is swallowed whole in an instant.

In spring and fall, the increase in diatoms is so great that the waters of current and bank areas become greenish. Diatoms glisten on nets and warps of longliners, schooners and draggers. They make decks slippery and the water itself becomes greasy to the touch. Such an abundance of food invites predators, and they are available.

The ctenophores, or sea gooseberries, appear in great numbers. They are about the same size and shape as a gooseberry and they are fishermen, or more accurately, anglers. They endlessly cast out lines, adhesive to the touch, which twist and turn in the water in blind search. Diatoms are stuck by the billion. Larval herring in the Bay of Fundy are caught and their bodies stacked like cordwood in the centres of the ctenophores' bodies to await digestion.

Planktonic life is extremely sensitive to temperature changes, and the collision between cold Labrador Current and the warm Gulf Stream can produce death on an enormous scale. The Labrador tends to dive under the Gulf Stream and then thrust up arms of cold water into the middle of the warm stream. This kills billions. Fishermen in the Grand Banks region often sail among a sea stinking of death with windrows of dead planktonic creatures and fish writhing for miles across the waters.

Tidal overturns, rips, clashing currents drastically upset the adjustment of plankton to habitat and may make planktonic creatures vulnerable to other hunters. A tidal overturn occurs twice a day off Campobello Island in Passamaquoddy Bay and thrusts up such a planktonic population – probably small shrimp – that thousands of seabirds squabble for a share of the harvest. Whales move back and forth, eating their fill.

Sometimes, deep water schizopods, or shrimp, born in the Gulf of Maine, are cast up on the shores of Campobello Island in such quantities that they are carted away for farm manure. In August, 1951, a great population of britt, or young herring, and copepoda occurred in the Bay of Fundy. The herring massed to feed on the copepoda which secrete fattening oil, and they ate so well that their excrement created oily slicks that covered the surface of the water over hundreds of acres.

The turbulent Bay of Fundy is unique in its range of habitats for plankton. The chaos of the bay's waters mean they are often rich in nutrient salts for plant growth. However, turbulence cuts down the chance of floating plants' survival. They cannot remain long in the top layers of the water where they would get enough light to grow.

But at the mouths of rivers (particularly the St. John) where heavy outflows of nutrient salts occur, phytoplankton blossom in their billions and large populations of fish exploit them.

The effect of the St. John River is so marked that it stimulates the entire southern life systems of the bay. Its outflow is strong enough to push supplies of microcrustacea into the outer part of the bay where they are available to large numbers of fish.

In Passamaquoddy Bay, currents keep the microcrustacea near the surface of the water, which is ideal for the herring, a shallows fish, and they teem there. Zooplankton born in the Gulf of Maine enter the Bay of Fundy and ease along the Nova Scotian coast. The further they penetrate the bay, the tougher conditions become as the phytoplankton diminish. The zooplankton do not enter the Minas Basin and it is poor in fish and plankton generally.

Between the Minas Basin and Shubenacadie, estuary conditions for the life of phytoplankton improve and so the numbers of fish increase. Theoretically, life conditions are ideal in the shallow inner part of the Petitcodiac estuary, but it is quite barren. The Petitcodiac tidal bore not only rips up silt from the bottom but thrusts up what microlife is living there. On the surface, it becomes easy prey for birds.

Although turbulence kills, or prevents much phytoplanktonic life in Fundy, precisely the reverse is true in the Gulf of Maine. There, great phytoplanktonic populations occur in April and May. In fact, surging populations occur throughout the summer along the Maine coast wherever there is turbulence. The reason for this is that the turbulence flushes up just enough salts from the bottom but does not create the turbidity that would make the photosynthetic process impossible.

In addition, the Bay of Fundy pushes out large quantities of water that is rich in nutrient salts because the supply has not been exhausted by plant growth. As it flows into the Gulf of Maine, much of its turbidity decreases, but the salts remain. These stimulate life production in the gulf which, later, will be fed back into Passamaquoddy.

In the end, the plankton may be seen as a microcosm of evolution. They evoke images of primeval earth, lacking animals, or even land-based plants, when oceans covered most of the globe, when life was struggling for the simplest forms of expression. It was, of course, on the teeming hordes of plankton that the higher forms of life developed and grew. From the plankton of the Atlantic shore, it is a short step to the next level of the food along the Atlantic shore—into the world of the herring.

A tow-net to catch plankton is easily made. For rowboat speed, the net should have a cone of cheesecloth about 24 inches long, a metal ring of 6 to 9 inches and a weight. A small cup at the end keeps the plankton from squashing on the mesh. Different size meshes catch different plankton.

 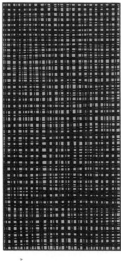  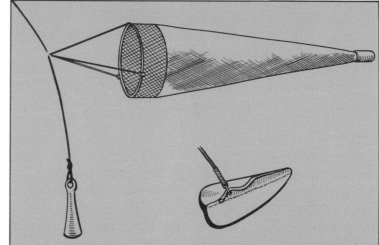

SURFACE WEIGHT   DEPRESSOR WEIGHT

11 BILLIONS OF SMALL BODIES

In 1859, Moses H. Perley of Saint John, His Majesty's Emigration Officer, checked all fishing in the Bay of Fundy for the New Brunswick colonial government. He found that herring spawned in immense numbers along a four-mile section of southern Grand Manan between July 15 and September 15. During heavy spawning, the water was as thick as porridge with eggs. When nets were raised onto the decks of ships, fishermen waded, slipped and fell, ankle deep in slithery eggs. The crews of more than one hundred fishing vessels fought each other for a share of the catch.

A Newfoundland fisheries officer, H. M. Piercey, was travelling by small boat down the Newfoundland coast near Notre Dame Bay on June 20, 1943, when he saw the biggest recorded spawning run of herring. The water along the shore was "almost white as milk." The discoloration, consisting of spawn and milt, extended up to a mile offshore. Piercey sailed for twenty miles down the coast and the sea was white all the way. Finally, when he rowed ashore, his oars turned up herring in the water at every stroke. Piercey had passed through at least twenty square miles of egg-choked sea.

The abundance of herring in the Atlantic region is a measurement of the immense size and scope of the food pyramid. The numbers of plankton cannot be measured or, in fact, comprehended, because they are usually invisible. But the herring are visible and measurable. They are the great intermediate layer of life in the pyramid which feeds on the plankton and fuels the higher forms of life.

A marine biologist, S. N. Tibbo, once checked a small herring spawning in a section of Chaleur Bay with skin-diving equipment. He calculated that 185,000,000 fish spawned there, with a body weight of about 55,000,000 pounds of flesh. This, he calculated, was less than one-quarter of all the herring available in the bay. Since local fishermen caught only about two million pounds of herring a year, their take of the total herring population was less than one per cent. By projecting these figures for all the Atlantic region, it is likely there are not fewer than 75 billion herring alive at any period.

The herring family is composed entirely of northern sea food fish which are the most common fish in almost all the marine environments in which they occur. The herring itself is probably the most abundant fish on earth. All members of the family, including the sprats, shads, alewives, pilchards, menhadens, reflect their common ancestry by close similarities at many periods in their development. The herring and the alewife grow up to eighteen inches (although it is a lucky herring that escapes fishermen's nets long enough to reach physical maturity) and the shad grows to about two-and-one-half feet. The alewife and shad enter fresh water to spawn but the herring does not, moving instead into shallow coastal waters to place its eggs in dense masses.

The herring has three main life stages, the first as a sardine. Huge but scattered schools of these sardines gather in coastal waters, particularly in Passamaquoddy Bay. The second period is the immature, or "fat" stage between two and four years of age. The fish then are scattered over any feeding grounds they can find, especially in the open waters of the Gulf of Saint Lawrence and over the offshore banks. In the third or mature "spawn" period, the young herring have joined adult schools. They are ready to collect into gigantic schools, move inshore and spawn.

The fish are caught year round in Passamaquoddy Bay, in Chaleur Bay, in the Northumberland Strait, in the shallows around the Magdalen Islands, along the southern portion of Nova Scotia, from Halifax to Yarmouth, and in Newfoundland on the south and west coasts in the winter and spring of each year.

The alewife, known as the gaspereau in the Atlantic region, is the most common anadromous member of the family entering the Atlantic coast rivers of North America. The run begins in Nova Scotia and New Brunswick in April, a couple of weeks before the shad begins its run. The spawning takes place in swift-running tributary rivers, and almost immediately after spawning, the adults return to the sea. The young alewives slowly work their way downstream and by the fall, the four-inch fish are in salt water. They remain at sea until they become sexually mature at about three years of age. There is a big fishery for alewives in the St. John River system, and also in the rivers of Kent County, New Brunswick.

The shad, which may weigh up to eight pounds, is most common in the St. John, Petitcodiac, Shubenacadie, Annapolis, Miramichi and St. Lawrence river systems. A shad migrating to spawn may cover several hundred miles in fresh water to reach its breeding point, although most spawning takes place fairly close to the estuarial area of the rivers. As with the alewife, not much is known of the three or four years of sea life which the shad spends in the ocean. In 1871, eastern North American shad were transplanted to the Pacific coast where they have thrived.

The herring of the Bay of Fundy are interesting for their ecology as well as their numbers. They live in moderate harmony with the intake of waters from the Gulf of Maine, the outflow of fresh water from New Brunswick rivers and various other circulations of the waters of the Bay of Fundy. They are so well adapted to this system that sudden changes in any of the components can seriously upset herring life.

Perhaps because of a severe drought which reduced the freshwater outflows of New Brunswick rivers in 1877, the main population of what was called fat "Quoddy herring" disappeared from the Passamaquoddy region. Apparently, they entered a cross-Fundy stream circulation and moved towards the shores of Nova Scotia. It took about one year for the entire body of herring to reach the Nova Scotian side and start moving east along the Scotian shore. The fishermen of Annapolis Royal had four years of fantastic fishing which ended abruptly in 1885, as the rearguard of the herring multitude passed on. In that year, the vanguard had completed the internal counter-clockwise circuit of the bay and had reached the outflow of the St. John River, thus returning to the general region of their original territory.

Despite the great numbers of herring-like fish, their movements and behaviour are frequently mysterious, their appearances and disappearances unexpected. The capelin, another fish closely resembling the herring in appearance, and with similar habits, personifies this fact. It is a member of the smelt family and virtually everything eats it, from many whales to the smallest seabirds. Other fish, particularly cod, follow them in their wanderings, feeding on them continuously. Seals and squid hunt them avidly. And, like the herring, the capelin appears in vast numbers, disappears, and leaves many question marks.

Capelin teem along the coasts of Norway, Spitzbergen, Greenland, Newfoundland, Labrador and Hudson's Bay, Alaska and the southeastern Russian coasts. They spawn most noticeably along the beaches of Newfoundland in June and July, often coming ashore in tremendous numbers and often becoming stranded in their efforts to get their eggs and milt embedded in the sand. Other populations spawn in deeper water, and on the banks areas. The spawning, like that of herring, is prodigious. Eggs may be piled up several feet deep along shorelines as the spawners are harried by cod, seals, and seabirds. Even when the capelin spawn in deep water, the eggs are hunted and eaten by haddock.

The Rev. Louis Anspach, an early 19th century observer, never forgot his first view of a capelin spawning: "It is impossible to conceive, much more to describe," he wrote, "the splendid appearance, on a beautiful moonlight night, at this time. Then, the vast surface of the Bay is completely covered with myriads of fishes, of various kinds and sizes, all actively engaged, either in pursuing or avoiding each other. The whales, alternately rushing and plunging, throwing into the air spouts of water; the codfish, bounding above the waves, and reflecting the light of the moon from their silvery surface, the capelins, hurrying away in immense shoals, to seek a refuge on the shore, where each retiring wave leaves multitudes skipping upon the sand, an easy prey to the women and children, who stand there with barrows and buckets, ready to seize upon the precious and plentiful booty; while the fishermen in their skiffs, with nets made for that purpose, are industriously engaged in securing a sufficient quantity of this valuable bait for their fishery."

A Newfoundland fisherman from Witless Bay, Bill White, has said that the Bay on the island's southeast coast is "black with birds," scores of thousands of them, when the capelin come in. One hundred years ago, schooner fishermen used capelin for bait, and when the capelin struck in to the beaches, the schooner-rigged "bankers" would come swooping out of the open sea like great birds to disgorge two or three thousand men. Some bankermen recall "seeing more dorymen in the bays than capelin." In a day, the men could scoop up a thousand tons of capelin. Within hours, the capelin would be hacked up and fastened to hooks that were dropped all over the Grand Banks.

The gathering of the spawning capelin triggers off a reaction throughout the sea. The cod which have spawned a few weeks earlier, recover condition by eating immense quantities of capelin. The salmon, moving steadily along the coastlines to spawn in rivers, feast almost exclusively on capelin. Seals become so bloated with capelin they are almost stuporous. Dogfish, plentiful in July, feed largely on capelin, and whalebone whales often have their stomachs distended with the small fish.

When the capelin "crop" fails, as has happened on odd occasions, particularly during the summers of 1932, 1934 and 1935, seabird colonies are hard hit and many birds starve to death. The ornithologist, Harrison F. Lewis, of Nova Scotia, noticed in 1935, when the capelin shortage was severe, that many young gulls were dead and dying along the shorelines of Nova Scotia.

The herring, capelin, shad, alewives, link the plankton to the rest of the sea, and their hurrying hordes are a testimony to the fertility of the sea. It is, however, the creatures in the next step in the food chain which most dramatically enforce this idea of fertility. The mighty codfish, and its environmental brothers, the haddock, the pollack, the hake, the redfish, and others, brought men to North America, and fed millions.

12 CODFISH AND OTHERS

In the latter part of the 19th century, after the cod had been fished ceaselessly for more than three hundred years, l'Abbé Ferland, in his *Journal d'un Voyage sur les Côtes de la Gaspésie*, was able to write: "It is the land of the codfish! Your eyes and nose, your tongue and throat and ears as well, soon make you realize that in the peninsula of Gaspé, the codfish forms the basis alike of food and amusements, of business and general talk, of regrets, hope, good luck, everyday life–I would almost be ready to say of existence itself."

The cod, which prowls every shoreline in the Atlantic region, is the most abundant of all the middle- and large-sized fish which follow in the wake of the herring billions. These fish include the codlike haddock, the silver hake, the pollack; bottom feeders like the witch flounder, halibut, American plaice, yellowtail and winter flounder and the deep-loving redfish; the pelagic fish (surface-feeders) such as mackerel; the anadromous fish (breeders in fresh water) such as the striped bass, salmon

The fertility of the sea hinges on teeming armies of plankton, microscopic plants and animals that are essential to the complex marine food-web.

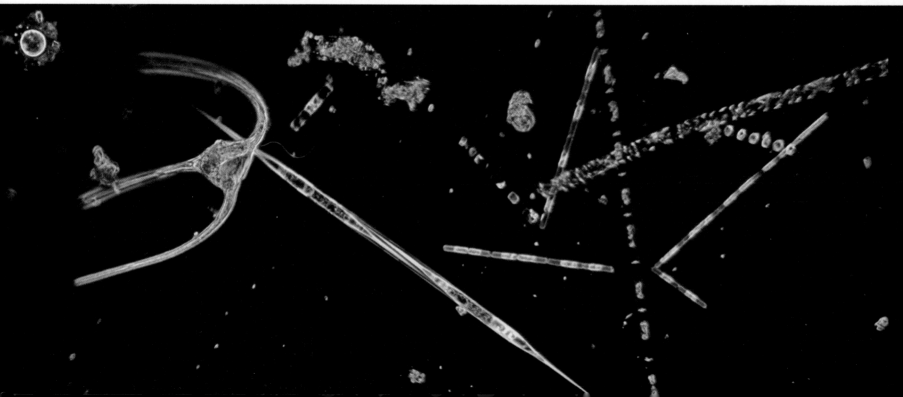

and sturgeon; the large surface cruisers, like the bluefin tuna, marlin, swordfish, the thresher, white and blue sharks, and the dogfish.

But the cod towers over all in numbers. Nearly two million tons of cod are taken from northern seas annually and there is no sign that this enormous catch dents their populations. They are caught by the millions as eight- and ten-pounders, but if they were allowed to live long enough, they would grow perhaps as big as the 211-pound fish caught off Massachusetts in 1895.

The cod are thickest on the banks areas, particularly on Grand Bank. The reason for the cod's abundance is twofold. First, it is enormously fecund. A female may carry nine million eggs at once. Second, it is omniverous. A cod will eat almost anything, including seabirds, bars of soap, old boots, pieces of metal, plastic and other codfish. This enables the cod to exploit almost any submarine environment. In northern waters, cod pick up spider crabs, amphipods, and pteropods in lieu of the small fish multitudes available further south. In Newfoundland waters, the cod eat launce, capelin, small dabs, eel pouts, sculpin and catfish. Offshore, other cod populations feed on young flounder, haddock, rosefish, alligator fish and herring. In coastal waters of Nova Scotia, Newfoundland, Prince Edward Island and the Bay of Fundy, the cod hunt scallops which they swallow whole, disgorging the shells after digestion. The Bay of Fundy cod are especially fond of small lobsters which they swallow tail first, nipping together the deadly claws as they go down backwards.

The cod eats selectively when it has to. In the spring, a large, capelin-eating cod may have a litre of the small fish in its belly as a means of filling out its liver, depleted by the long winter draw. The capelin catch gives the cod a dose of fat, but the big fish also needs protein. When the squid begin their run for the shore (also in pursuit of capelin) they are full of protein and the cod gorge on them until surfeited.

Cod spawning has not been seen anywhere in the Atlantic region but it is thought that the biggest spawning area is probably off the east coast of Newfoundland and Labrador and on the offshore banks. Some small-scale spawning also occurs somewhere along the south and west coasts. The spawning season is from March to October. Sable Island cod spawn from the first week in March but on the cooler Grand Banks, the fish probably spawn in June. When the fish appear inshore, they almost certainly have spawned, and are on a feeding migration.

The ideal spawning temperature of the water is between one-and-a-half and seven degrees centigrade. A cod egg can hatch at zero degrees but at nine degrees hatching will take place in about forty days. During the egg and larval drift period in Newfoundland, the youngsters are pushed southward by the currents. The young cod is helpless as it hangs underneath the yolk that feeds and supports it during the first days of its life. By the end of six days, the yolk is mostly absorbed. The small fish develops a mouth and immediately begins to feed on phytoplankton. This is the critical period in the codfish's life, a time that will determine later abundance. If weather conditions have delayed the hatching of the cod for a few days, the phytoplankton may have grown too big for the young cods' mouths and the fish may starve to death surrounded by food. But if all goes well, there is another period of drift before the young cod sinks to the bottom.

Between four and five years of age, when the cod is about eighteen inches long, it enters the fishery, but during its early growth period, its movements are mysterious. It may stick fairly close to one territory or it may, unaccountably, make a long migration—up to one thousand miles—perhaps in a search to satisfy its voracious appetite.

The cod is ideally fitted to exploit all levels of the sea. It scrunches up shellfish as easily as it hurls itself clear of the water in mad pursuit of herring or capelin. It moves up, down, back and forth in response to its hunger. The haddock, on the other hand, a close relative and superficially difficult to distinguish from the cod in appearance, is less adaptable. Its jaw is underslung for feeding solely at the bottom and this adaptation restricts its range, its numbers, its success generally. It frequently shares territory with the cod, particularly on the eastern banks areas. Haddock concentrate in summer on the Grand Banks and move northward. Gatherings appear along the east coast of Newfoundland but their habit of concentrating so thickly makes them extremely vulnerable. In July and August of 1950, capelin spawned heavily along the southeast edge of the Grand Banks and this attracted an equally great concentration of haddock feeding on the capelin eggs. Fishermen quickly found the haddock. Almost the entire fleet of European and Newfoundland trawlers hit the haddock. In six weeks, enormous catches were obtained.

Ten years later, the Russians discovered another concentration of haddock on the Grand Banks. They caught 60,000 tons of haddock in 1960, 40,000 tons in 1961, 3,000 tons in 1962 and thus obliterated that population.

Both cod and haddock are extremely vulnerable in the immediate post-spawning period but cod survival is more stable. Entire year-classes of haddock may be wiped out when larval haddock are carried into deep water by currents. Alternatively, there may be huge survivals, causing the ocean to teem with haddock. In 1949, the survival rate was high on the Grand Banks. In addition, an accidental drift and survival onto St. Pierre Bank created a fishery there for the first time. These 1949 year-class fish came into the fishery in 1955 when all haddock catches began rising steeply.

The cod and haddock are resembled, again superficially, by the pollack which looks like a cod and which is common off southern Newfoundland, at the mouth of the Bay of Fundy, and in places on the Scotian banks. It is highly mobile and an individual may spend the summer in the region of Campobello and then dash south for the winter to hunt off Cape Cod. The silver hake shares at least part of the pollack's habitat on the Scotian banks and in the Bay of Fundy, perhaps due to its fondness for herring and mackerel, but it is not a great traveller.

All fish, as demonstrated by the haddock with its underslung jaw, have made adaptations to fit them to their environment, none more than flatfish which hug the bottom and whose backs are camouflaged to deter attack from above. They occupy various depths, the winter flounder hugging the coasts in shallow waters, the yellowtail flounder prowling further offshore, in depths of roughly 150 feet, the witch flounder going down to about 1000 feet, and, finally, the American plaice living in submarine strongholds as deep as 2500 feet.

The Atlantic halibut is also a flatfish, but it has liberated itself from bottom feeding, and ranges through all depths in search of prey anywhere. Like the pollack, it is a great traveller. One fish, tagged at Anticosti Island, made a rapid journey across banks, channels, and deep ocean, to Iceland, 1600 miles away. The halibut, like the cod, is an omniverous feeder (its appetite sometimes boosts its weight to half a ton) and it has a special adaptation to assist the survival of its eggs. It lays two million eggs in deep water and the eggs drift up to "float" at median depths, protected from hunters which might eat them at the surface or on the bottom.

The redfish, or rosefish, a slow-growing species which can take about ten years to grow ten inches, has found a place at the six-hundred-foot depth mark along the fringes of banks regions, most commonly along the continental slope from the Grand Banks up to Labrador. It is also adaptable enough to rise to the surface to feed at night (it is sometimes found in Bay of Fundy waters in as little as thirty feet of water) and its young, which are born viviparously from May to August, also rise to the surface and hunt there until they are an inch long when they sink back into the Stygian depths of a thousand feet or more.

All these fish are basically exploiters of the sea bottom. They are not comfortable feeding at the surface, even though prey may lead them there. The real surface hunters, or pelagic fish, are totally different in appearance, habit and temperament. One of the most dramatic is the swordfish which migrates into maritime waters in June, swimming at medium-shallow depths until a school of fish appears illuminated against the surface. The swordfish rises swiftly, hurtles out of the water, and lands with a percussive smack that panics the school fish. As the prey dart back and forth, the swordfish flails its sword among them. After the carnage, it cruises back and forth eating fragments of flesh.

Another specialist is the tuna which is not a banks fish and does not have a predictable migratory pattern. It does not school but it can't be said to be a loner, at least not until it reaches about four hundred pounds. In the western hemisphere, its birthplace seems to be the Caribbean from whence it wanders, often moving at high speeds, north into the Atlantic shore region, and elsewhere. One tunafish, tagged in the Caribbean, turned up fifty days later at Norway.

The surface hunters are almost always great travellers, ranging far and wide in search of prey which, usually, is itself at the mercy of uprisings of plankton populations. The thresher shark, waving its enormous flail-like tail up to seven feet long, cruises in search of any gathering of herring, mackerel, or squid which it can herd into tight groups and then cut off pieces with its tail. The white shark, a warmth-loving active fish, ventures onto the Scotian shelf in search of seals moving back and forth to Sable Island, or sturgeon heading for the rivers of New Brunswick, or tuna on their summer cruises, and with its great bulk, up to forty feet long, can overturn dories and drown fishermen when provoked.

The surface hunters nearly all relish mackerel, itself a pelagic fish, which literally vacuum-cleans the surface of the sea for every particle of food it can find. Mackerel gather in schools which, in early times, were twenty to thirty miles long and more than half a mile wide. Their presence anywhere in the Atlantic region—particularly in the Gulf of Saint Lawrence—invariably provokes an enthusiastic reaction by whales, porpoises, sharks, tuna and men. As a result of men's hunting, the mackerel's great abundance has been seriously impaired. For every twenty mackerel prowling the Atlantic shore in the 1880's, only one hunts today.

The bottom feeders and the pelagic hunters have exploited the sea from the surface to the deeps. Another group has adapted to use fresh water to start new generations of their kind. These are the larger anadromous fish (as opposed to the herring-like freshwater spawners) which are abundant along the Atlantic shore. The striped bass, which may reach seventy pounds, is a voracious hunter of nearly all small fish, crabs, squid, worms and other creatures. It spawns in the Miramichi, along the Nova Scotia coast, in the Bay of Fundy and even prowls the St. John River region in mid-winter where it may be caught by

fishermen and pulled out through the ice.

It is, however, the salmon which most captures the imagination. Its family includes trout and char, and it probably was once a migratory fish of the Arctic. Perhaps through geological or climatic change, salmon left the Arctic and established themselves throughout European, Asian and North American waters. Given clean water, a place to spawn, they are tremendously fecund. Before the advent of dams and pollution in rivers and streams, they were common enough both in Europe and North America to be a food for domestic help as well as for kings. The salmon of the Atlantic region, unlike the Pacific coast salmon which spawns once and dies, can spawn for many years.

Mature salmon enter several hundred streams and rivers throughout the Atlantic region and Labrador, waiting in deep pools for their spawning move. They may have to jump rapids, weirs, waterfalls and dams but their strength can send them spinning twenty feet or more in mid-air. They are thickest today in the Miramichi River in New Brunswick where 30,000 die on anglers' lines each year compared with 20,000 in all Newfoundland and 12,000 from the Quebec rivers.

When salmon reach the place of spawning—at, or close to, where they were born—the male and female work together to build a nest, or redd, on a gravelly bottom. The female turns on her side and fantails a hollow about eighteen inches deep. The male hovers nearby, presumably on guard. Once the redd is finished, both fish sink into it. The female lays her eggs, the male

Sharks have curious combinations of primitive and advanced characteristics and different reproductive methods. Males have claspers on the pelvic fin for internal fertilization, a more up-to-date method than spawning. Some sharks produce living young, with the embryo developing from the yolk

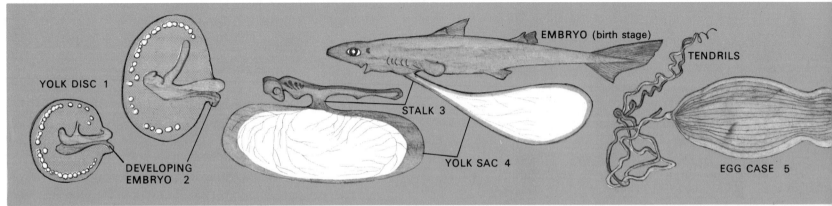

spills milt over them. A female salmon expels roughly eight hundred eggs for every pound of her body weight.

Mortality is high in this period because of the ordeal of getting upstream, and of the spawning act itself. Once spawning is completed, the adult fish either seek the refuge of deep pools to overwinter, or make their run for the sea.

The salmon eggs hatch the following spring to become fry, or alevins, and begin a slow growth to adulthood. As parr, they hunt microscopic life in the streams, taking about seven years to grow seven inches when they are ready for the sea. They head downstream in the spring as smolts, possessed by a special energy that sends thousands of them into the sea every night.

Their sea sojourn is mysterious. The only certain thing about it is the great growth the salmon makes. It becomes a voracious hunter, especially of herring, and after only a year at sea, it may weigh six pounds. After two years it can weigh twenty pounds and reach forty pounds in five years.

When the moment comes for salmon to return to the rivers of their birth, they are in beautiful condition–"A storehouse of energy," as one biologist put it recently–and they begin the first river runs before the spring floods. The first run of fish is in prime condition and prized by all fishermen. Their bodies are blue-black, their flesh pink and firm. After them comes a second run, the grilse, or jumpers, which are one-year-at-sea fish. They weigh from three to six pounds, are thin and graceful, and they can make tremendous jumps. After them again comes run upon run of salmon, all mature fish. The running slows in August, and then picks up again in September and October.

These larger anadromous fish, and the smaller ones, echo the past when they either lived in fresh water and then extended their ranges into the sea, or vice versa. They include some fish which became trapped, as it were, by the rapidity of geological change. Both Newfoundland and New Brunswick hold ouananiche, salmon which are landlocked completely and live in rivers which have barriers that prevent them from reaching the sea or in lakes which now have no outlets. They are prisoners, like some populations of the Arctic char which are landlocked in several Newfoundland and New Brunswick lakes. These geological barriers have redirected their normal habit of living in fresh water for six years before taking a sea change.

Finally, there is the Atlantic shore's one catadromous creature, the American eel, which lives most of its life in fresh water and only returns to the sea to breed.

The plankton bloom in the Labrador Current, on the banks everywhere; the herring teem in the Passamaquoddy, the Magdalen shallows host the hurrying hordes of mackerel; the cod move across the Grand Banks in their billions; the great threshers, the swordfish, the marlin, the tuna run north in pursuit of this rich source of food. These are manifold examples of the success of swimming fish. There is, however, one last form of life which took a different evolutionary path, settled permanently to the bottom and stood fast. These are fish with shells.

disc (1,2) until it lifts away from the yolk, still connected by a stalk(3). After birth the young shark feeds on the yolk disc, slowly absorbing it(4). Others produce egg cases whose tendrils attach to plants while the embryo within is feeding on the yolk(5,6). Cross-section of an adult male (7).

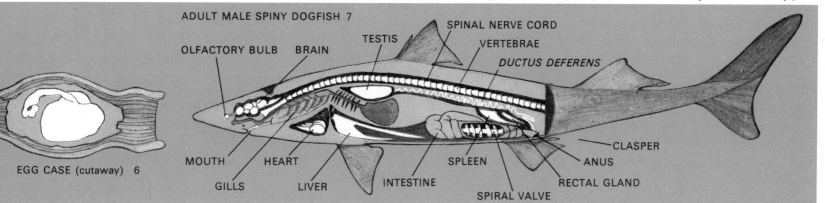

ADULT MALE SPINY DOGFISH 7

OLFACTORY BULB   BRAIN   TESTIS   SPINAL NERVE CORD   VERTEBRAE   *DUCTUS DEFERENS*   CLASPER   ANUS   RECTAL GLAND   SPLEEN   INTESTINE   SPIRAL VALVE   LIVER   GILLS   MOUTH   HEART

EGG CASE (cutaway) 6

13 FISH WITH SHELLS

Since the Cambrian period, shellfish have been one of the most successful forms of life on earth. They have colonized the deepest parts of the sea, lakes, streams, tidal mud, and sand. They include the crustacean lobsters, crabs and shrimp, and the molluscan clams, oysters, barnacles, mussels, scallops and whelks. Their lives in the Maritimes reveal the reasons for their 500-million-year success story on earth.

Shellfish give a hint about the mortalities and dangers of ancient seas, millions of years before mammals or even reptiles appeared on earth. They sacrifice billions of lives to ensure the survival of hundreds. When the oysters in the warm shallows of Malpeque Bay, at Prince Edward Island, are spawning in the late summer, they release trillions of eggs. Few survive to become adult oysters. This massive release of eggs is also an exercise in dispersal, a constant thrusting at the boundaries normally limiting the survival of shellfish populations, indeed, of all populations. The floating shellfish eggs, drifting on tides and currents, pushed by the wind and the Coriolis force, may perish in unimaginable numbers but they are also constantly ready to exploit any new opportunity offered them in the sea. This, too, is an ancient principle of life.

It has been estimated, for instance, that during the Cenozoic period in the Pacific, about 30,000,000 "rafts" of floating debris were sent drifting from islands and mainland masses, and that about 3,000,000 contained animal life. Only about 30,000 of these "rafts" reached land and only about three hundred of these successfully landed animal migrants. This tiny survival number, spread over several million years, was sufficient to populate many islands with new forms of animal life.

The shellfish of the Atlantic shore illustrate this dispersal principle today. In late 1953, a large bed of scallops was discovered on the St. Pierre Bank, southwest of Newfoundland, and fishermen took one hundred tons of scallop fish out of the area the following year. They were warned by scientists that this population was the result of a single, incredibly successful "accidental" spawning. A large quantity of scallop larvae had drifted accidentally into the St. Pierre area where the young shellfish settled. But it would not likely happen again for hundreds, or even thousands, of years.

Shellfish, or, more accurately, shelled fish, teem throughout all ranges of the Atlantic shore in such diversity that no simple explanation of them can do justice to their ingenious penetration of sand, mud, shingle, seaweed, ocean depths and tidal flats. To simplify, they consist basically of molluscs, which include the snails, clams, squid (the only real swimmer) and various others like the coat-of-mail shells and tuckshells. They also include the crustaceans like crabs, lobsters and barnacles, and the echinoderms, among which are numbered the starfish, the sand dollar, the sea urchin and the sponge.

The Atlantic shore is a splitting ground for both the Arctic and the warm water species of shellfish. The southern gulf is warm enough for oysters to spawn, but deeper, colder waters in the northern gulf may contain millions of sub-arctic shellfish, like Iceland cockles, Arctic wedge clams and polar starfish. These creatures cannot stand warm water but a boreal group, more tolerant, can live in shallow or intertidal waters throughout the Atlantic region. These are the periwinkles, limpets, common moon shells, giant scallops, soft-shell clams, shipworms, lobsters and purple starfish.

The temperate species are ideally suited to the splitting ground of the region since they can withstand winter freezing and yet seize the opportunity to breed in the brief weeks when water temperatures are between sixty and seventy degrees. The shallow lagoons of Prince Edward Island, and the Northumberland Strait region are swarming grounds for many of these creatures, including quahogs, dwarf surf clams, odostomes, and various snails.

Finally, the high temperature group which cannot stand prolonged winter icing, like the bay scallop, the fallen angel wing, the green crab and the horseshoe crab, reaches the region of Sable Island and into the Bay of Fundy, but no further.

The biology of most shellfish is a game of chance in which the sea is infused with quadrillions of young shellfish drifting helplessly, willy-nilly, wherever wind, storm, current or tide may take them. For colonizing purposes, the shellfish uses quantity as a means of survival. Its behavior is complex and of high "quality." On a typical stretch of shoreline – particularly in the Bay of Fundy—barnacles abound, at least one billion of them for every mile of some shoreline. Barnacles are one of the few free-swimming forms of life that have degenerated, or de-adapted, into sedentary existence. A young barnacle may spend hours searching for exactly the right place to settle when it is in its larval, free-swimming stage, and about to begin adult life. Once settled, with its head down so that a cement-producing gland can be stuck firmly onto the rock, the barnacle is ready to develop into a headless, tail-less animal. It lies on its back and opens and closes a protective circle of plates, using its legs to beat food into its digestive system.

The Bay of Fundy, with its circulating currents, is ideal for barnacle reproduction. When the larval forms of the common rock barnacle settle in June and July, the rocks look as though they are covered with a white powder. In response to these great numbers, the bay is also infested with several kinds of predatory whelks.

The shellfish, in their long history, have developed the capacity to dig in sand, like clams, and even to swim, like scallops. The scallop opens its shells wide, claps them together, and forces twin jets of water out of the corner of its hinge. This pushes the shellfish forward with its shells open wide in readiness for another "bite" out of the water.

The scallop—three-quarters of all Maritime scallops live in the waters near Digby, Nova Scotia—is odd in another respect. It provides a refuge for two most unlikely guests, the young sea snail and the common hake. The youngsters live inside the valves of scallops and when danger threatens from predators, five or six of the youngsters may jam into a single scallop.

The scallops spawn in late summer or early fall. Each female sheds about a million tiny eggs. Simultaneously, the males shed milt, or sperm, which so densely permeates the water that most of the shed eggs are fertilized immediately. As soon as the eggs are hatched, the young scallops start a free-swimming stage with the oceanic plankton which lasts about three weeks. At the end of that time, when the young shellfish are about the size of a pinhead, they "sound," or settle to the bottom. At the end of their first winter, the young scallops measure about one-fifth of an inch in diameter. It takes between five and nine years to reach a shell diameter of from four to five inches. A really large scallop—eight inches in diameter—may be seventeen years old.

The complexities of shellfish biology are still being revealed to scientists. The Maritimes have oddly-placed populations of oysters—an isolated colony at Mahone Bay, midway along Nova Scotia's Atlantic coast, some small colonies at Musquedoboit, Cape Breton, and around the Magdalen Islands, with the main populations occurring in the Prince Edward Island region, the home of the famed Malpeque oyster. The placement of these isolated colonies, separated by hundreds of miles of intervening and fatally cold water, is another clue to the Hypsithermal period of circa 7000 years old.

The sperm of the male oyster contains a hormone which may trigger spawning in the female. Spawning begins at 68 degrees. The females clap their shells gently together about twice a minute, and with each clap they "blow" out a mass of eggs. The males, meanwhile, have opened their shells slightly and let out a steady, hardly visible flow of sperm—"like curls of smoke from a cigarette," as a marine biologist describes it.

A few hours after the oyster's egg is fertilized, it turns into a tiny oyster larva which can swim by vibrating a number of tiny cilia, or hairs, and so joins the floating planktonic life of the surface. It is possible to plot its capacity to colonize. It joins a current which, at best, travels between ten and fifteen miles a day. Within thirty-six hours, the young oyster has developed shells, and within four days, it has turned pale red. It has, theoretically, travelled up to fifty miles. At ten days, it has turned dark brown, and has gone one hundred miles. By the end of three weeks, it is the size of a grain of pepper, is visible, has eyes and a foot that can project from the shells to drag the young oyster over stones and rocks. At this period, it is ready to settle. At the most, it has travelled 210 miles.

The settling of the young oyster is carefully adapted to finding the best places for survival. The tiny shellfish swims back and forth, crawls over objects like stones, pieces of waterlogged wood, grass stems, and swims off if it is not satisfied. Desirably, the little fellow would like to find a place where there are other oyster larvae. When the ideal place is found, the oyster lies on its left side, extrudes a spot of cement which flows between shell and hard surface and securely anchors it.

Although shellfish are mainly sedentary, a number are surprisingly mobile. The commonest method of travelling is by pumping blood into their so-called "feet," a tongue-like protuberance best known in the steamer clam, which enables them to inch to safety into the sand. Razor clams, for instance, are so adept at this that they can bury themselves in a minute in sand. Surf clams, on the other hand, often come out onto the beaches at night and wander along the shoreline, propelling themselves by flipping their "feet" with convulsive movements which jerk them an inch or so forward. This is probably less wandering than pure flight because burrowing snails, which hunt at night, are likely to bore through the sand in search of them.

The world of the shellfish is a study in mass mortality and ingenious hunting methods. The walrus herds of 17th century Sable Island, and the Magdalen Islands ate about six hundred tons of clam necks, or tongues, every day. Shellfish are a delicacy for almost any form of life that can crack their shells. Smooth whelks, so common in some parts of Passamaquoddy Bay that they plough the sand like tractors in search of their prey, dig down nearly a foot for soft shell clams, drill a hole through the clam shell, poke in a proboscis, and clean out all the flesh. They can, if they catch a clam on the surface at night, raise a bump on the back of their foot, place the clam there, then dig down to safety before the day-hunting gulls begin their work.

The masses of blue mussels, clustered thickly together on rocks throughout the Atlantic shore region, look invulnerable until smooth whelks appear at high tide and drill into them.

The oysters of the southern gulf, massed on eelgrass, on rocks, on other oyster shells, seem equally invulnerable until starfish appear, wrap their tentacled arms around the shellfish and slowly pull them apart. The ocean quahog, massing by the million in deep waters throughout the gulf region, seem to have the safest place of all until voracious wolffish appear and crunch them up like peanuts. Scallops, resting on sandy bottoms off western Nova Scotia, are methodically swallowed by prowling codfish. Flounder, moving inshore as the tide rises, watch for the breathing necks of buried clams and nip them off. Eels, loitering in the shallows before entering the deeps to breed, grab the neck and wrench it clear out of the buried shell.

Crabs love shellfish, and their hunting method is typified by the green crab. It makes an indentation in the sand, kicks away at a sand face, and gradually works its way down to the buried clam. Right behind it are often two sand shrimps waiting for a chance to feed at remnants as the crab nips the clam shell open and begins feeding.

The oyster is a true "crop" for men to harvest, a niche it shares with the ubiquitous lobster which has colonized much wider territories and is harvested even more efficiently than is the oyster. The lobster is, perhaps, three hundred million years behind the oyster in evolution, appearing first in the age of dinosaurs, the Triassic, two hundred million years ago.

In the southern part of the Gulf of Saint Lawrence, the lobsters lay their eggs in two bursts; the first in June and July by old-shelled lobsters; the second in August by lobsters which have shucked off their shells earlier in the summer. To lay eggs, the female lobster rolls on her back and raises the front part of her body. The eggs are extruded through two tiny openings at the bases of her second pair of walking legs. The eggs, six to eight abreast, ooze down into a pocket formed by the lobster's curled tail where they stick to her swimmerets. Between the last two pairs of her walking legs is located the sperm sac which, at that stage, is filled with sperm deposited by the male during earlier mating. The eggs (which may number 75,000 in an eighteen-inch-long female) are fertilized as they pass over the sac.

The eggs remain protected under the lobster's tail for nearly a year as they mature and get ready to hatch. Again, in the southern gulf, the big hatching periods begin around mid-June, reach a peak in July, and continue through September. The numbers of young lobsters hatched run into the billions. The tiny creatures are about one-third of an inch long, reddish in color, and perfectly adapted to swimming. They rise, and swim at or near the surface where they join the planktonic hordes and, presumably, are eaten by some of the larger plankton. They free-swim for up to two months, molting and shedding their skins three times to reach a length of half-an-inch. They are then perfect, miniature lobsters.

Although their numbers are incredibly large, predation is equally prodigious. All during their free-swimming period, they are eaten by almost every young fish in the sea. After they settle, they are eaten by small fish, crabs, even other lobsters. As they grow, they become, if anything, more vulnerable. At the four-and six-inch sizes, for instance, they come to the attention of cod, skates and dogfish, and at that size, they are a real delicacy for the larger lobsters. Once they reach twelve inches long, however, they are reasonably safe from wild predation. Their worst enemy then is man. He catches and eats most of them over the years. Few lobsters die of old age in the Maritimes.

Like the codfish, a lobster is almost truly omniverous. In captivity, scientists have kept them alive on dog biscuits. In the wild, and in captivity, a lobster which has caught too much food to eat at one time will bury it like a dog and then stand guard over its hidden prize.

All lobsters observe territory, a device which keeps them nicely scattered over the available living areas, but they are very slow feeders and when an unexpected abundance of food suddenly becomes available, like a large dead fish, the territorial rules are abrogated. The lobsters collect to feed, but when the feast is over, they disperse back to their own territories.

The lobster uses its claws like a bulldozer blade. With them, it digs burrows and uncovers clams in the sand. In the Northumberland Strait area, it uses the claws to dig refuges in the sandy bottom. The claw is powerful but not strong enough to crack a clamshell outright. Instead, the lobster sets the clam on edge and nibbles away at the sharp edge of the shell with its mandibles until it has broken off enough shell to get at the soft flesh inside.

The squid of Newfoundland is a true natural history phenomenon. It is included with the shellfish here, not because it is a shellfish but because it is in flight from its shellfish origins. The squid is an escapee – probably it developed like the lobster in the Triassic period – from millions of years of wholly defensive and passive life. It has become an active and aggressive predator.

It is an extraordinary animal, a mystery. Nobody knows where it spawns, no spawn has ever been found. It does not spawn anywhere near the coast of Newfoundland, and it is most unlikely that it spawns anywhere on the Grand Banks. Its numbers are immeasurable. Fishermen report seeing squid at the surface for mile after mile of sailing.

To the human eye, they bear hardly any external relationship to any other living thing, except octopuses and their allies. The body of the squid is tubular, terminating at one end in a triangular-shaped vane which controls depth and direction. At the other end is a thick mass of "arms" which spring out in a circular pattern.

Inside this mass of arms is its hydraulic jet apparatus that gives the squid high speed. However, the jet engine seems to be at the wrong end. It drives the creature tail first. It is the only hunting creature in the world which backs up to its prey.

The squid are accompanied by herds of pilot whales which, collectively, eat hundreds of tons of them every day without measurably depleting the host populations. When they reach the shores of Newfoundland, the squid fall in among the capelin which either are spawning, or have finished spawning, on the coastal beaches. The meeting of capelin and squid is a hunter-victim confrontation like no other in the area. The carnage is Jovian. Shredded capelin flesh floats over many square miles of sea. The squid does not attack frontally; it backs slowly through the water parallel to its capelin victim, keeping slightly behind it so that the capelin is not triggered into flight. At the moment of attack, the squid turns its tail towards the capelin by firing a set of diagonally-set jets in its mouth, and hydraulically blasts itself backward. The movement is almost too fast for the human eye to follow. At the last moment, the squid turns its body sharply and its head, beak and tentacles spin around before it bites and kills the capelin.

Squids are completely oceanic creatures with no affinities for land. They collide with Newfoundland and thousands of them become stranded on the beaches. After the initial strandings, the squid hordes prowl the shores but no more strandings occur. Some scientists feel they have learned the danger of the shore. Fishermen are agreed that the squid is the most intelligent of all sea creatures. Since they have a life span of only one year, they have many other lessons to learn in order to survive even that long. The pursuit of the pilot whales and tuna is an irritation but the squid soon "learns" to seek refuge in water that is too shallow for the whales or the tuna. These are the squid-jigging grounds of song and legend in Newfoundland for more than two hundred years. In this refuge period, fishermen catch up to two thousand tons of squid for codfish bait.

During the ninety-odd days that the squid occupy the coastal strand, they grow at high speed, quintupling in size. By the time the call comes for retreat, usually in November, they are about twelve inches long. Then, it is theorized, they are ready to breed. They pour back over the Grand Banks, not pausing or hesitating. Quite suddenly, they are gone completely. They breed and die as mysteriously as their progeny will appear again the following year.

Forest animals

Every animal has adapted to a specific area of the forest — the small rodent scurrying about in his underground tunnel, the tree-climbing mammal, and the bird high in his treetop nest. Most animals will vigorously defend their niches in the forest, especially during breeding season and in the fall. Although very few spend all their time in the deeply wooded areas, the rich second-growth forests of the Maritimes offer an abundant food supply; an individual territory is extremely important to some animals during the food-gathering months.

Deer mice fill their cheekpouches with balsam fir seeds and then hide them for future use.

Young moose twins browse on the lush vegetation to be found in forest clearings and fringes.

The flying squirrel can glide up to 150 feet, ▶ using its tail to change direction of flight.

A slow animal on land, the porcupine is an efficient climber, feeding on bark and leaves.

Our most common warbler, the yellow warbler, prefers thickets and forest fringes, yet is often found in the shrubbery around houses. A male may sing over 3,000 songs a day in the summer breeding season before winter migration takes them far south.

▼ As large, well-built predators, goshawks are capable of killing prey the size of rabbits and pheasants. They hunt at low levels, but build their bulky nests of twigs lined with bark high up in the trees, and usually return to them each year.

The red-breasted nuthatch nests by making a cavity in a decaying tree, smearing the entrance with pitch.

Forest birds

The forests of the Maritimes region offer a great variety of living spaces where specific types of birds have their own nesting sites and even closely related families often occupy different areas. Year after year in the breeding season, birds will return to the same jealously-guarded territory, and the song of the male notifies other birds that the area is occupied. Territory must satisfy not only nesting and protection needs, but also provide adequate food for the family. The majority of birds feed on insects; even those that eat grain as adults feed insects to their young. Predatory birds prey on the abundant small rodents of the forest floor. Birds with specialized-looking beaks will feed predominantly on one type of food.

The sparrow hawk rests with its prey, a deer mouse. ►
It nests and may live year-round in the Maritimes.

On Great Island, puffins have honeycombed every usable square foot of earth with their nesting burrows.

Seabirds

Great varieties of seabirds are attracted by the rich fishing grounds of the Atlantic shore, and after wintering at sea or in far-away lands, the birds move towards the shore or off-shore islands to nest. Year after year, during the breeding season, birds in their great numbers return to the same rocky ledges, giving names like Bird Rock or Gull Island to the area. The craggy surface of Funk Island may be completely hidden by huge armies of murres, returning annually to nest in the same territory. Up to 100,000 tons of phosphates and nitrates in the excrement of seabirds are added to the Atlantic region each year, thus increasing plankton growth and fish populations.

◄ *The razorbill, far left, can be distinguished from the murre by its thicker, white-marked bill.*

► *The high cliffs along the maritime coast provide the main Canadian nesting sites for the great cormorant.*

14 BIRDS OF SEA AND SHORE

In the very early spring the seabirds of the Atlantic shore move toward the coast and offshore islands. They have spent six months at sea, riding out winter gales, surviving sudden freeze-ups, escaping predatory fish, seals, whales and men. They have flown great distances to hunt, and some birds have been to Mexico, South America, Africa, the Mediterranean, Norway and northern Russia. Now, their movement to the shore is a very specific act. Most of them return to the same burrow or to the identical rocky ledge where they bred the year before.

The murres, most numerous of the auks (which include puffins, razorgills, guillemots) move toward a score of breeding places. A million or more birds encircle Funk Island, decorating the sea and the sky with wild nuptial dances and chases. Another horde heads for Baccalieu Island at the tip of Conception Bay in Newfoundland. A third group occupies another bleak rock, Green Island, off Witless Bay on the Avalon peninsula. About five thousand murres take up their places at Cape St. Mary's on the south shore of Newfoundland. Elsewhere, thousands more head for breeding places on islands along Quebec's south shore, on the tall cliffs of Bonaventure Island, the Gaspé, and along the Nova Scotian coast.

Everywhere seabirds gather to breed, there is spectacle and sound. The murres, massing together on Funk Island, obscure its rocky surface while the roar of their voices is not unlike the close-up sound of Niagara Falls. The few non-fishermen to reach Funk Island report being overwhelmed by the experience. The fishermen claim that the sound, the stench, the numbers of birds can drive a man mad.

The murres lay their eggs on bare rock but their close relatives, the puffins, are more specifically adapted. They dig deep burrows on any island where they can find soft, excavatable earth, a fairly difficult feat on rocky Atlantic coasts. The puffins find their earth on Great Island, off Witless Bay, where scores of thousands have honeycombed every available square foot of earth with burrows. More than 100,000 occupy Perroquet Island near Bradore on the Quebec south shore. Other colonies range down the New Brunswick and Nova Scotian coasts as far south as Machias Seal Island in the Gulf of Maine.

The remaining auks, the razorbills and guillemots, are not very common, perhaps because their nesting possibilities are limited by the difficulty of finding burrows among tumbled masses of shoreline rocks. Their populations are in the very low thousands compared with the million-plus numbers of puffins and murres.

The second great seabird population is rarely seen near land, never seen at their nesting colonies in daylight. These are the Leach's petrels. Sailors have a better name for them, Mother Carey's Chickens, and once believed they contained the souls of fishermen lost at sea. Their nesting headquarters in the Atlantic region is on Gull Island, again in Witless Bay south of St. John's, where an undetermined number of birds breed–variously estimated at up to more than a million–in countless tiny burrows. In summer, the entire island reeks of musk from oil the petrels secrete. To avoid such hunters as gulls, falcons, and others, the petrel visits its breeding colonies only at night, even though it is a diurnal bird and has difficulty in seeing and flying well at night. Gull Island is uproarious when hundreds of thousands of petrels come in from the open sea to sing and dance above the island before they go to ground to relieve their mates who have spent several days in the nesting burrows awaiting their return. The petrels also strike inshore at scores of other places throughout the Atlantic area; at tiny islands with a few inches of excavatable soil; at the tops of the cliffs on Bonaventure Island; at Kent Island in the southern end of the Bay of Fundy.

The murres spend their winters wandering offshore, particularly on the Grand Banks. The puffins prowl all shorelines in winter. Petrels criss-cross the Atlantic, perhaps ranging the eastern shores of Europe and Africa. The gannets, which are the third greatest seabird population, spend their winters along the Florida coast and in the Gulf of Mexico. These magnificent white and gold birds with a wingspread of up to six feet move north very early. Many of them fly with migrating geese, heading for Bonaventure Island where the tops of the cliffs are eventually smothered with twenty thousand birds. They fly to Cape St. Mary's or Baccalieu Island, or Bird Rock–more than one hundred thousand birds–in the Magdalen Island chain, or Funk Island which is the most northern colony.

Each of these three great seabirds exploits the marine environment in a different way. The murres and puffins land on the surface of the water, dive, then swim underwater using both their paddle feet and wings to run down a great variety of small fish. As they "fly" underwater, they are sometimes caught by large cod, seals and other submarine predators fast enough to overtake them.

The petrels do not dive, but hover at the water's surface, dangling their dainty paddle feet. They seem to "dance" on the surface as they look downward for planktonic forms of life, tiny fish, or oily waste thrown from passing ships. When necessary, they can go for days without food.

If the murres and puffins are flying submarines, and the petrels are helicopters, then the gannets are dive bombers. They drop from a height of one hundred feet or more to strike streamlined beaks vertically into the water. Apparently the dive performs two functions; it scatters and terrifies schools of fish and plunges the bird below the depth of the fish so that the prey is reflected against the surface of the water.

Life at sea is harsh and seabirds are among the toughest of all birds. Long before they can fly young murres jump off nesting cliffs up to five hundred feet high and fall straight down to rocks or water where they bounce without apparent injury. An adult murre hunted by a peregrine falcon may put up such a terrific struggle that the falcon flies off without finishing the kill. Young petrels are deserted by their parents while they are still in the burrow, usually in the late fall. They must get out of the burrow at night, learn to fly, then head offshore in pitch blackness. Young gannets must launch themselves from high cliffs and fly immediately. At Cape St. Mary's and at Bonaventure in the early fall thousands of anxious young gannets line up along the cliff tops and look down at the great drop before them.

The strength of seabirds is essential since they wander so far across the earth. One of the greatest fliers is the shearwater, a bird closely related to the Leach's petrel. Shearwaters arrive in Newfoundland and Nova Scotian waters in May; unlike all the other seabirds, they are "wintering" in the north, having bred in the southern hemisphere, most notably at Tristan da Cunha. Their arrival coincides with the inshore migrations of squid, herring and capelin. The shearwaters are killed by the thousands by fishermen who know their obsessional appetite for cod livers. The fishermen throw the livers in the water and use poles or gaffes to brain the shearwaters as they scramble heedlessly for the feast.

The eider ducks of the Atlantic shores are one of the few seabirds to have accommodated themselves to man's presence completely. Traditionally, they cluster along the east coast of Newfoundland in the winter. There, two or three hundred thousand strong, they dive at the edge of the ice pack in search of shellfish. For the past two hundred years, one bird in every six has been killed by duck-loving Newfoundlanders without any noticeable decrease in their numbers.

The kittiwake, a small, dainty gull, is the last major seabird in the Atlantic shore and numbers about five hundred thousand. The birds nest anywhere they can find suitably steep cliffs. They breed in gullies on Funk Island and on the highest cliffs throughout the Gulf of Saint Lawrence. They decorate the cliffs like thousands of white-clothed apartment-dwellers relaxing on their balconies. They are wanderers rivaling the albatross and move easily from Newfoundland to Greenland, or to Scotland, Denmark, Norway and the Russian north coast. Like the eiders, they make excellent table birds and until recently thousands were shot or taken from nests as youngsters but as fast as the shore people ate them, more kittiwakes moved in from Greenland and elsewhere. Today, however, Maritime cooks use processed foods on the dinner table and the kittiwake is safer than it has been for a good many years.

The great auk once occupied the same ecological niche in the northern hemisphere as the penguin does in the south but only its bones are left, and on Funk Island puffins still kick great auk bones to the surface as they dig their burrows. Among Newfoundland fishing folk, the extinct bird is the subject of enduring legends.

When Nicholas Denys was on the Grand Banks in the 17th century, he saw the great auks hunting, before men began to kill them systematically. "The great auk," he said, "is . . . variegated in white and black. It does not fly. It has only two stumps of wings with which it bears upon the water to aid in fleeing or diving. It is claimed that it dives even to the bottom to seek its prey on the bank. It is found more than one hundred leagues from land, where nevertheless, it comes to lay its eggs, like the others. When they have had their young, they plunge into the water; and their young place themselves upon their backs, and are carried like this as far as the Bank. There one sees some no larger than chickens, although they grow as large as geese. All these birds are considered good to eat by fishermen. As for myself, I do not find them agreeable. They taste of oil because of the quantity of fish and of livers they eat; and they serve to make fish oil. The fishermen collected them for this purpose. There are vessels which have made as much as ten to twelve puncheons of it."

The oceanic-ranging seabirds have a vital ecological function that probably significantly affects man's works in the Atlantic area because of their great numbers. Seabirds have always provided meat and eggs but this supply is no longer exploited energetically as TV dinners reach northern tables. However, most of the five or six million seabirds in the Atlantic region eat their own weight in food every day. Their excrement, packed with nitrates and phosphates, is therefore voluminous. The outpouring of excrement from Funk Island alone is around twenty thousand tons annually. For all seabirds in the Atlantic region, it is probably close to 100,000 tons. Phytoplankton cannot live without phosphates and nitrates. The seabird contribution must enormously stimulate planktonic growth, particularly in the Labrador Current and Grand Banks regions. This must, in turn, create reactions in herring and capelin populations and thence in populations of cod, seals, whales and so on down through the chain.

With their great colonies and overpowering numbers, the seabirds are truly creatures of the sea. Between them and the landbirds are the birds of the shorelines which are much easier to find and watch than the seabirds. When Charles W. Townsend, an ornithologist, was surveying the birds of New Brunswick in 1912, he noticed there were very few herring gulls in the harbor of Saint John. Today, thousands of them circle the city, stand on roofs, squabble over garbage from ships and offal from net fishermen working in the harbour.

The herring gull is not, strictly speaking, a shorebird because it lives anywhere—offshore, at the shore, inland. The bird is a 20th century success story along almost every Atlantic shoreline. It has increased through its opportunistic capacity to exploit any food resource—garbage dumps, clam beds, shrimp hordes, worms, blueberries, offal from fish-processing plants, eggs and nestlings of any other bird, or carrion. It is a member of a big family which includes many gulls that resemble it in appearance—the glaucous gull, the Iceland, Kumlien's, the ring-billed, the laughing, Franklin's, Bonaparte's, the little, the ivory, Sabine's, and various terns. But the herring gull is far more numerous than all the others combined.

Its breeding headquarters in the Atlantic region is Kent Island, near Grand Manan, where a burgeoning colony of sixty thousand birds gathers during the summer. Other colonies are strung along every coastline. Unlike most colonial-nesting birds, the herring gull is not averse to nesting alone. It has colonized interior America, including the Great Lakes, and wanders great distances. One bird in its lifetime might prowl both the shores of Labrador and the eastern coast of Mexico.

The herring gull is not alone in responding to man's presence in the shore region. Bonaparte's gulls—small black-headed birds—have in recent years begun loitering during the summer along the southern gulf from Chaleur Bay to Tormentine. Biologists believe that this may be an exploratory population which will eventually breed in the region. The ring-billed gull, which is an interior migrant of continental America, oriented towards the Mississippi system, seems to be spilling eastward into the Atlantic region, also finding the southern gulf a good spot for the summer. It has been found breeding near Bathurst, New Brunswick, and it may soon become a resident shorebird.

Black-headed gulls, on the other hand, seem to be steadily moving into the Atlantic region from Europe. They have begun wintering in Nova Scotia and it is assumed that although they leave the Atlantic shore for the summer, perhaps to return to Greenland, or Iceland, for breeding, they will eventually become established in Nova Scotia or New Brunswick.

The black-backed gull, larger than the herring gull and originally much warier, is undergoing a revolutionary change in both its behaviour and distribution. It is increasing rapidly everywhere, has changed from being a winter resident of the southern Maritimes to being a year-round resident. It is now at least ten per cent of all gull flocks.

The other gulls are insignificant in numbers. The laughing gull, the Sabine's gull, the ivory gull, are seen rarely and then only as individuals or in small flocks.

The real shorebirds are nowhere near as noisy or as ubiquitous as the gulls. Plovers, turnstones, woodcocks, snipe, whimbrels, curlews, sandpipers, willets, yellowlegs, knots, dunlins, dowitchers, stilts and phalaropes use the Atlantic region either as a breeding territory (all are migrants) or as a resting area during migration. These birds are prowlers of the shallows, tidal flats, beaches, barrens; the tireless searchers for tiny crustacea and worms. They are great fliers. When they touch down in a typically Atlantic shore environment–a quiet, glass-smooth inlet at Cape Breton or a broad expanse of tidal flat in the Bay of Fundy–they bring with them a wild memory of the ends of the earth, of Arctic tundra and Patagonian grasslands.

The golden plover is the most celebrated of the shorebirds because it was once so numerous and was a delicacy in the cooking pot. John James Audubon once saw millions of them at New Orleans where 48,000 were gunned down in one day. The golden plover migrates from South America (usually Patagonia) up the Mississippi, but returns east of the big river. It came down through the funnel of the Bay of Fundy in great numbers but near the end of the 19th century it was being rapidly shot out. Today, it numbers only a few thousand although it is increasing slowly. The plovers may be seen tarrying on the tidal flats of Fundy before they cross the Nova Scotian peninsula to take one giant non-stop flight into South America.

The Eskimo curlew was even more abundant than the golden plover. Flocks took hours to pass a given point, but this curlew is only a memory. It was shot out in the late 19th century. It has a modern counterpart in the Hudsonian whimbrel whose habits resemble it closely. The Hudsonian has also been hunted mercilessly. The slaughter was especially large at Cape Breton and in Richmond County, Nova Scotia, where the whimbrels loitered to fatten up on barrenland berries. The Hudsonians were still pouring into this "refuge" area in the early twentieth century, but between 1900 and 1920, their numbers were reduced from thousands to hundreds. It is more common in Newfoundland where hunting pressure is lighter.

The knot, another sandpiper, also was once numerous and then made scarce; not so much by hunting in the Atlantic region as by organized torchlight slaughter at Cape Cod in Massachu-

The early stages of feather formation resemble the scales of fish and reptiles (1). The feather pulp splits up (2) and the plumes show as on a newly-hatched chick (3). Interlocking barbs make the wing airtight (4). Special feathers (5) maintain airflow and prevent stalling.

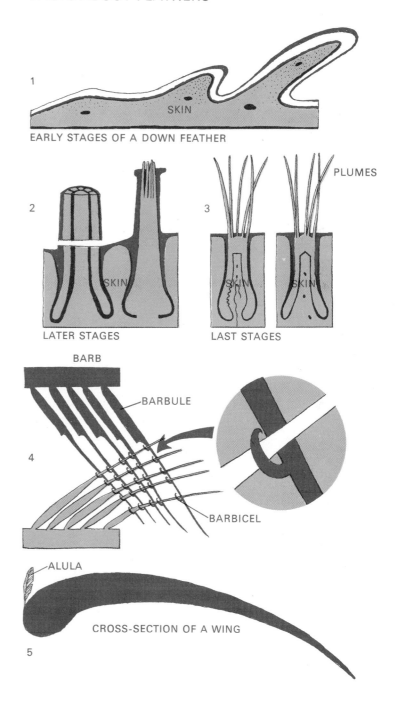

FACTS ABOUT FEATHERS

1
SKIN
EARLY STAGES OF A DOWN FEATHER

2
SKIN
LATER STAGES

3
PLUMES
SKIN
LAST STAGES

4
BARB
BARBULE
BARBICEL

5
ALULA
CROSS-SECTION OF A WING

setts. In 1897, knots were selling in Boston markets for ten cents a dozen.

The Migratory Bird Treaty of 1916 has done much to save the shorebirds from obliteration. Rigid prohibition and control of hunting was necessary since almost all shorebirds stop and hover over bodies of shot comrades, enabling hunters to destroy flocks of thousands. World-wide changes in habitat, however, have made it unlikely that primeval abundance will ever be regained in the Atlantic region even with controls.

One of the reasons for former abundance is because shorebirds–like seabirds–are relatively long-lived, and are able to exploit efficiently the many environments they pass through in journeys of thousands of miles. A plover may hunt beetles in Patagonia, worms in Honolulu fields and insect larvae in the Arctic. A knot, arriving in the Arctic before the spring thaw is over, eats saxifrage buds and old crowberries from the previous summer. It is the crowberry, which thrives in many Atlantic shore areas, that draws down thousands of shorebird migrants in the fall, the fuel which sends them south.

The sea- and shorebirds of the Atlantic region are perfect examples of environmental adaptation. Each bird fits neatly into a niche. It is, of course, this precision of adaptation that has made so many of them vulnerable to environmental changes made by man, yet in most, it is a strength which ensures survival. The legs of the common sandpiper are just long enough for it to dart into the shallows and pick up food in a retreating wave on a Prince Edward Island beach. The legs of the stilt sandpiper, on the other hand, are long enough to prowl tidal lagoons in the Bay of Fundy during low tides. The shearwaters glide on wings that have grown enormously, disproportionate to their short stocky bodies, in response to the need for gliding thousands of miles across the open sea. The herring gulls' omniverous guts are dynamic adaptations at work, sending them constantly into new territorial opportunities. The whitewinged scoter, a seagoing duck, has a gizzard which can crush shellfish. The oystercatcher has a beak that can thrust into a partially-opened oyster, cut its shell-closing muscle, and rip out the flesh in one deft motion.

The list of ingenious adaptations could be prolonged almost indefinitely. They make the birds of the Atlantic shore and sea areas endlessly colourful and fascinating to the observer.

15 THE GREAT MIGRATION

The entire Atlantic region lies in the path of a great migration route as birds hasten to and from the ends of the earth to breed. It is also an area of great internal migrations involving other creatures, caribou, many kinds of fish, and insects, so that the phenomenon is more visible along Atlantic shores than anywhere else in Canada. That does not make it any less a mystery. No single theory can yet satisfactorily explain the puzzle of migration.

Migration may occur because of the geological theory of continental drift–which gradually separated habitats of birds, forcing them to fly seasonally to preserve the availability of food, or it may be simply an expression of a biological urge, of the continued pressure of populations into areas where the best chances for species survival occur.

This brings up the second great query about migration: how? There is no agreement here either. It may be celestial navigation, in which birds use the stars, the sun or the moon. It may be sponsored genetically, or it may be some combination of the earth's magnetic fields operating on the migrants' sensory apparatus. And it may be all these things. Whatever it is, the migrants are incredibly precise navigators.

The migration of birds along the Atlantic shore is a double spectacle. In spring, it is landbirds pouring north in successive waves. In fall, it is shorebirds pouring south in streams. The spring migration can be measured by species, or groups of species. The song sparrows arrive around the night of March 24 at Wolfville, Nova Scotia, or during the night of March 29 at Sackville, New Brunswick. Behind them is a flood of horned larks, grackles noisy in gusty grey skies, robins fleeing across the Northumberland straits to Prince Edward Island, redwings, fox sparrows and cowbirds appearing in the Annapolis Valley and along the shores of northern New Brunswick.

The killdeers reach into southern New Brunswick and Nova Scotia early in April, and their arrival signifies the beginning of a lull for the migration of songbirds. The lull is promptly taken up by the arrival of waterfowl–blue- and green-winged teal, scaup, wood ducks, baldpates, American widgeon. As the waterfowl are building up numbers on dozens of feeding points, the songbirds recommence their arrival–winter wrens, white-throated sparrows, ruby-crowned kinglets, savannah-sparrows–all during the month of April.

Penultimately come floods of warblers, some of them arriving in late April, but the bulk of them flying into central New Brunswick and Nova Scotia by the middle of May, reaching Prince Edward Island and Cape Breton by around May 20, the Gaspé by the end of the month, and Newfoundland by the beginning of June.

Last of all come the yellow-bellied flycatcher, the sharp-tailed sparrows, and the red-eyed vireos.

The swallow is the longest-migrating landbird. For several years, some barn swallows nested under a bridge at Shoal Harbour in Newfoundland, a territory they returned to each year from wintering grounds five thousand miles away, probably in Argentina. Their migration along the last few hundred miles must have been lonely since the barn swallow is a rarity anywhere in Newfoundland.

Most landbirds are content to fly into the U.S. southern states, or to Central America for their winters. The bulk of shorebirds, however, is committed to huge migrations. The greater yellow legs, a common Newfoundland breeder, heads deep into South America for the winter. The dowitcher heads for the West Indies and Brazil. The semi-palmated sandpiper swings down into Central America and the sanderling and buff-breasted sandpiper reach Patagonia. The red phalarope may stop over in Florida, or it may push on into the open sea for South America.

The Bay of Fundy, with its great expanses of littoral, ideal for feeding and resting shorebirds, has been called "a migration funnel," through which pass hundreds of thousands of birds during the spring and fall. The pace of the migration is often hectic. During April and May, big flights of geese and ducks pass through the bay, flying day and night, depending on the suitability of the weather.

Almost before the night-flying northward migration of landbirds has eased, the southward migration of shorebirds has begun. The shorebirds have forced deep into the north to snatch a brief few days of summer to breed fast, and then get out. The Bay of Fundy is host to their returning multitudes. Sandpipers sweep down both shores in compact mobs. Plovers and dowitchers gather at feeding places, mingling with yellowlegs and other species of shorebirds.

Migrants clearly use diverse navigation systems. Thousands of warblers, working up through New Brunswick, across Fundy, over Nova Scotia, Cape Breton, into Newfoundland, and further north, are navigating by the stars. They only migrate at night and become demonstrably disoriented on misty or cloudy nights. Herring gulls, and gannets taken from nesting islands in the Maritimes by scientists and transported hundreds of miles away into strange territory, infallibly head back home when let free. This proves the power of navigation but it does not illuminate why young herring gulls, dispersing from the nesting colonies of their birth, may migrate north in the fall, or west, heading as far inland as Chicago. Nor does it explain how Leach's petrels–tiny, ground-burrowing birds of the open sea–find their way hundreds of miles in darkness, and in thick mist, to nightly meetings with their mates in the burrows.

Migration is so dramatic and so visible that few Atlantic shore people are insensitive to it. On the shore, they see warblers landing exhausted in their gardens, or watch smelt dashing up nearby streams to spawn. On any moonlight night, particularly in the Fundy area, the night sky resounds to the cries, calls, twitters, squeaks and chatters of scores of thousands of migrating birds.

Until very recently, Maritimers insisted that sudden and unaccountable disappearances of creatures were due to migrations. For centuries, lobsters were thought to be migrants because they disappeared abruptly from inshore fisheries. But when they were tagged by scientists, their migratory capacities proved to be nil.

The great populations of starfish were assumed by fishermen to be migrant–in search of food–because of their capacity to appear abruptly and decimate shellfish populations. The scientists proved that a starfish's top speed is only one foot an hour, and the average starfish does not move any more than about twenty yards in any direction. Then skin divers in tidal areas where currents were strong observed that starfish rolled themselves into "wheels" and bowled along the bottom like kids' hoops.

It is clear that creatures move in response to manifold needs, adaptations, pressures. As the season changes from winter to spring, flounder migrate, working their dark, flat-topped bodies up from the middle depths into twenty or thirty feet of water, bright with spring sun. During the winter, they have lived (like many fish responding to cold) partially comatose, eating very little. When they feel the pull of the shallows, they advance along a front thousands of miles wide.

Snipe migrate hastily. They winter in the southern states of the U.S., or further south, and hit the Maritime region during the first or second week in April. The migration seems to be controlled by the moon. In their fall migration, they usually begin flying south during the first quarter of the moon. The main body of the birds is on the night wing during the full moon, and migration tapers off during the waning period.

In bad weather, migration becomes an epic tragedy for wildlife. Many migrating birds can fly above mist and storm to navigate accurately. This may explain why warblers and sparrows, incapable of above-the-overcast flights, become so disoriented in mists and die in collisions against lighthouses all along the southern shores of Nova Scotia and New Brunswick. It may explain why gannets never seem to get lost; as high-soaring birds they can reach above the mist and storm. It would explain why puffins, never high-flying birds, so easily get lost during coastal fogs.

Lighthouses are terrible traps for migrants. Ralph Maker, chief keeper on Grand Manan Island, says that bird deaths on foggy or rainy nights are sometimes so great that he feels bound to collect the bodies by the bucket-load and dispose of them. "Often," he says, "I get a dozen bucket-loads. Thousands of those little brown birds must be injured and die out there on the sea."

For predators, migration time means great hunting. The hunters–hawks, owls, and crows–gather at lighthouses. The crows march around the rocks methodically swallowing every crippled bird they can find. Hawks settle and eat their fill. Even owls, attracted by the sheer number of victims, gather in daylight to hunt them.

The migrants also fall at sea in uncounted numbers. Leamon Harvey, a Grand Manan fisherman, has watched migrant birds –mainly warblers and sparrows–dropping exhausted on the decks of fishing boats for more than half a century. "Without my boat," he says, "I suppose all those thousands of little fellows would die."

On Grand Manan in bad weather, the small migrants blanket the rocky shoreline ledges at low tide. There, they are destroyed by thousands of gulls.

Creatures migrate "voluntarily" and involuntarily. True migrants move along predetermined paths towards breeding places or winter rest territories. Involuntary migrants are victims of storm, cold, food shortage or disorientation during real migration. A Chicago-centred storm may push Mississippi River migrants into the Maritime region. Bad weather in the Gulf of Saint Lawrence and around Newfoundland has driven seabirds, especially murres, as far west as Montreal. In the early part of this century, such an involuntary migration was observed by a Quebec shore hunter named Napoléon Comeau. In November, 1904, he reported seeing dovekies migrating *westward* along the coast for two weeks, probably in response to bad weather conditions along the east coast of Newfoundland. He watched thousands die of hunger and exhaustion. Earlier, they had migrated to Newfoundland when weather conditions got tough in Greenland, their breeding home.

Migration in the Atlantic region is an all-encompassing phenomenon. Cod, for instance, can migrate hundreds of miles. On the Grand Banks, they move from warmer southeast waters to the cooler northwest as the summer progresses. The extent of cod migration was revealed by a series of cod-tagging experiments, conducted between 1927 and 1940, that added new puzzles to the phenomenon of migration. Why did all the cod in the coastal waters off Shelbourne, Nova Scotia, stay there between 1927 and 1930–except for one fish which swam to the St. Pierre Bank in 1927? Why, out of thirteen hundred cod tagged near Halifax in October, 1934, did one fish end up off the north coast of the Gaspé Peninsula? In April, 1937, one thousand fish were tagged off Sable Island. Why, within five years, had they spread to the three winds–one to Newfoundland, three to the Gaspé, two to Cape Breton, one to Halifax, and two in the general direction of the Grand Banks?

Many migrating birds are sensitive to temperature; a north-advancing warm front in the fall may take thousands of migrants north with it. The cod is susceptible to oceanic temperatures. It may be trapped in a restricted area by cold-water barriers and starve, although, on occasion, vast numbers of medium-sized fish have broken through the cold-water barrier to reach the surface in pursuit of capelin. This "migration" often ends at the inshore fishery. The cod may winter in deep, comparatively warm, Atlantic water with a quarter of a mile of icy Arctic water above it. Many areas off the coast of Newfoundland contain just such warm-water pockets below the cold Arctic layers and cod migrate to find them. In May and early June, they migrate again to spawning grounds, and, finally, they migrate in search of food, such as capelin, eaten in quantity.

Fish migration covers thousands of miles and rivals that of the hemisphere-ranging Arctic tern which flies up to 20,000 miles a year. Tuna, swordfish, dogfish, sailfish, and sharks are the long-distance champions but in August, 1961, a female oceanic puffer left some sort of a record when it was washed up onto a Newfoundland beach. It had swum, or been carried, from the North African coast southward in the Canary Current, and had entered the general water circulation of that area. Then it had been caught up in the westward movement of the North Equatorial Current and had reached the West Indies. From there, it had joined the Gulf Stream and somehow, probably at the collision point between Labrador Current and Gulf Stream, had spun off and entered the Newfoundland current system.

The journeys of the Canadian harp seal and the Newfoundland caribou are unique expressions of the migration process in larger animals. The seals pour down out of the Arctic to whelp on the ice in the gulf and off Newfoundland shores. Soon after they have finished, they work their way back into the Arctic while the caribou, which have calved in the Newfoundland southlands, are moving north again to spend their summer in the northern highlands.

The migration of the harp seals is on a grand and dramatic scale, involving as many as two million animals which will give birth to their new families on ice stretching from the Labrador down the coasts of Newfoundland, and deep into the heart of the Gulf of Saint Lawrence. The southern movement begins in the fall and the seals usually reach the Strait of Belle Isle around New Year's Day, already fat, and in fine condition for spring whelping on huge ice floes building up in the gulf.

At the tip of Newfoundland, the seal hordes split. Some move down the eastern coast of Newfoundland; others move into the Gulf of Saint Lawrence through the strait. During January, their movements are something of a mystery but they probably range widely. By late February, enough ice has built up in the gulf and off the coast of Newfoundland for whelping to begin. The animals start coming out of the sea and take up positions across thousands of square miles of territory. By the last days of the month, the seals have collected on the ice in groups as big as six thousand breeding animals to the square mile. (A patch of ice can be as big as one hundred square miles in area.)

There are two main breeding areas. The exact locations vary somewhat from year to year, depending on weather conditions. One is in the gulf, north of the Magdalen Islands and west of Bird Rock. The other is somewhere in the region of Belle Isle. It may be as far east as the Funk Island territory, or further north, near the coast of Labrador itself.

The moment the pups are born they show how their lives are adapted to survival on the short-lived ice floes of their birthplace. In two weeks, their weight rises from about twenty pounds at birth to more than one hundred pounds. Their foetal white coat is firm, or fast, as the fur industry would have it, for only fourteen days, and then it sheds, turning grey-black and blotched. At about this time, the pups are deserted by their mothers and must fend for themselves. Soon after, they start their own migration into the Arctic for the summer, trailing the returning adults.

The harp seals migrate by far the greatest distances—more than one thousand miles southward—in search of whelping territory, but this journey is by no means an uninterruptedly southern movement. The harps, like practically all ocean-going seals, are extremely flexible. They can make emergency journeys of three and four hundred miles a week in search of whelping ice, or perhaps food.

The grey seal, of which there are probably fewer than five thousand in the Atlantic shore region, are also great migrants, but in totally different fashion. After whelping on Sable Island, the main body of perhaps three thousand animals disperses, like the herring gulls of Kent Island, almost to the four winds. Hundreds of them reach the shores of Quebec and Newfoundland, and a few even reach the Labrador.

Meantime, the harp seals are not long in the Arctic before the caribou are preparing for their southern migration. Early in September, the velvet on the horns of bull caribou has dried and rubs off as they polish their antlers clean on stunted larches. All caribou become sleek and fat. The rutting season begins in October. When the fall frost comes, the caribou work their way south again, the time of the migration depending mainly on the severity of the season.

Among the greatest migrants are the whales of the Atlantic shore, although their movements are at the moment imperfectly understood. The fin whale, perhaps the commonest whale of the region (roughly six thousand animals inhabit the continental shelf waters), moves north and south in spring and fall, perhaps in search of euphausid populations. The sperm whale lives further offshore, along the edges of the continental shelf, and dives deeply for squid, but its northern migration of males deep into Greenland waters while females remain further south with their youngsters is puzzling. Both the bottle-nosed whale and the sperm migrate into Sable Island waters, perhaps both of them hunting squid, at various times of the year. All the other whales–the sei, the blue, the humpback, the right, the minke– make short or long migrations which, with the heavy hunting pressure of the 18th century gone, seem to be increasing throughout the Atlantic shore waters.

The small pothead whale migration into shallow waters is probably the most dramatic, certainly the most visible, since it gives men an opportunity, in eastern Newfoundland, to drive them inshore like sheep where they strand on beaches and are slaughtered for oil and flesh, up to five thousand of them at a time. Finally, the greatest migrant of all, the killer whale, which seems to migrate anywhere that fancy and food take it , killing seals at Arctic ice holes, chasing dolphins at Sable, following whale-hunting vessels out of Blandford, Nova Scotia and Dildo, Newfoundland.

The migration of caribou, seals and salmon are dramatic but birds remain the greatest migrants, or accidental travellers. The records show that, given the right conditions, no journey is impossible. There is even the record of a kittiwake *swimming*

across the Atlantic after its wing was broken. The yellow-nosed albatross is strictly a southern hemisphere bird, yet a number of them prowl the northern hemisphere. At least two have been shot in the Maritimes, one in 1884, and another in 1913. Southern bald eagles from Florida, fresh from the nest, often head north to prowl the coasts of the Bay of Fundy. One bird, born at the end of January, 1942, left the Tampa region in late February and was shot at Leger Brook, New Brunswick, about thirty days later.

Manx shearwaters, albatross-like birds which nest in the eastern Atlantic, wander or are driven into the Atlantic region. That is an easy journey for an oceanic-flying shearwater, but white pelicans which arrived in the Bay of Fundy during the late 1800's were another matter.

Not all bird migrations are on the wing. Thousands of murres nesting north of Newfoundland drift south with their youngsters who cannot fly until they are three weeks away from the nest.

The most extraordinary of all migrations, however, involved a shorebird, the lapwing. One population of lapwings customarily spent the fall and early winter feeding in mid-northern England, and when it became chilly there, they moved over into central Ireland to spend the rest of the winter. In December, 1927, a flight took off from England and headed for Ireland. What happened next is not documented but it is thought that Ireland was completely blanketed by fog. The lapwings, navigating visually, overflew Ireland and when the fog cleared, they found themselves still over the sea. They kept going for eight hours or more. As shorebirds, they could not, of course, land or float on the sea. Some undoubtedly reached Greenland and perished. The main body hit Newfoundland in mid-December, and stragglers flew on into Nova Scotia. They had flown into a winter like nothing in their experience or capacity to withstand. The last birds lingered on into mid-January, 1928, before the disaster of the lapwing migration was ended.

Migration seen across the broad panorama of the Atlantic environment, is thus the most complex of all the natural historical phenomena. It is a visible, dynamic and exciting product of millions of years of life in this environment, through the ice ages, the rising and falling seas, the ceaseless change of biological process seeking constantly new expressions of its life.

A SANCTUARY IN THE SEA

Sable Island and its unique natural history attracted the interest
of Dr. Donald Gunn, a Canadian psychiatrist and amateur naturalist,
shown above touring the island. Dr. and Mrs. Gunn obtained government
permission to visit the island and spent three weeks photographing
the natural life and recording the breeding sounds of the Ipswich
sparrow. One significant fact of many in this interesting island is
that it is the world's only breeding ground of the Ipswich sparrow.

Blowing sands

Sable Island, located 100 miles off Nova Scotia's coast, is a sailor's nightmare. This sliver of sand, a mile wide and 16 long, is surrounded by numerous shifting sand bars 6 to 12 feet below the surface. Since the 16th century they have been responsible for over 500 shipwrecks and 5,000 deaths. Only half of the island is stabilized by grass, and waves and currents are continually pushing the sands eastward. Though its rate of movement is slower today, the island shifted six miles between 1766 and 1899.

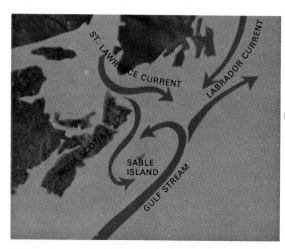

◄ *Two major currents colliding cause whirl-pool or deadened currents, depositing the sand that eventually formed Sable Island.*

► *If wind and storms uproot the vegetation, a blowout occurs, and plants may not re-establish themselves to hold the sand.*

▼ *An aerial view of Sable Island. Part of the large sandy area on the right used to be farmland for the lifesaving station.*

The lifesaving station, abandoned to the elements over twenty years ago.

The lighthouse keeper's house and light on the centre of the island.

Struggle to survive

For three hundred years pigs, cattle and horses escaped from the numerous ships wrecked on the sandbars of Sable Island, and the island is a famous home of wild, once domestic, animals. The pigs ate everything washed ashore, dead or alive, but the population of horses varied with the food supply. Shrubs and grasses, always at the mercy of winds, make up the menu on this treeless island. Pictured on the opposite page, hardy marram grass struggles to colonize new patches of sand (1); horses graze on the sparse grassland (2); the decaying carcass of a horse adds nutrients to the sand and richer vegetation grows until the nutrients are leached from the sand (3); a shy little pony (4) interrupts his meal to take a peek at the photographer, Dr. Gunn.

Of seals and sparrows

Dr. and Mrs. Gunn were surprised to find a young harbour seal asleep on the beach (A), as this wary animal usually flees at the approach of humans. When Mrs. Gunn nudged it with her shoe (B), the seal awoke from its slumber and waddled back to the sea (C).

The Ipswich sparrow (overleaf), a larger version of the Savannah sparrow, is faced with possible extinction. This hardy bird which migrates in the winter as far south as Georgia has already outlived numerous predators such as rabbits, cats and foxes, which man unwisely introduced to his summer home and only breeding ground, Sable Island. But the island itself is gradually being washed away and in 200 years may disappear altogether. The Ipswich sparrow may go with it.

A

B

C

PART FIVE/ CONSERVATION

16 A DAMAGED LAND

The appetite of the spruce budworm for the foliage of evergreen trees became enormous in the early fifties in New Brunswick. To combat it, the Federal Government aerially sprayed DDT on millions of acres of commercially valuable balsam fir forests. The poisonous spray, about one pound of it per acre, killed a lot of budworms, but it also played havoc with all the rest of the forest environment. Unselectively, it killed almost all insects and so removed the prime source of food for forest-haunting birds such as kinglets, vireos, warblers, crossbills, wrens and creepers. The birds were also hit directly by the DDT.

The poison filtered on downwards into the streams of the Northwest Miramichi watershed where it killed most aquatic populations of caddisflies, stoneflies, mayflies, blackflies and midges, all in their larval stages. These larvae are the only source of food for fish, and the salmon of the Miramichi were caught in a famine area. The DDT also killed the fish outright. Within two days of the spraying, masses of dead, dazed and dying salmon were seen along the banks of streams everywhere. As the young salmon and brook trout died, songbirds fell dead from the trees.

The DDT was sprayed in June, 1954. By August, it was clear that of the millions of salmon which had been spawned and hatched from the gravel beds of the Miramichi in the 1953-54 period, not one fish had survived. An entire year-class had been wiped out.

The Atlantic shore region has been occupied by men for more than four hundred years and in that time it has been transformed from a primeval to a man-made—or at least, man-oriented—environment. It has been an example of what one ecologist recently called "a world-wide upheaval of flora and fauna." Man has fitted into the ecological picture, very like an animal, clustering wherever the fertility of the environment is highest, seeking out his own niches and transforming the landscape around him. For instance, one hundred years ago, a south coast Newfoundlander could take an axe in hand and walk a mile or two to cut enough wood to build a dory. Today, he may have to power-boat thirty miles to reach a millable tree.

Man's depletion of the original resources of the Atlantic region has been severe. Heavy fishing has diminished the size of most of the individual oceanic fish with any commercial value—the pollack, cod, haddock, rosefish, halibut. In the early days, one-thousand-pound halibut were common. Today, the average fish is nearer two hundred pounds. Cod were once forty to one hundred pounds. Now, they average six to eight pounds.

Exploitation has drastically reduced the numbers and variety of creatures. The once-abundant great auk is extinct and the rare Labrador duck has gone. The passenger pigeon is extinct too, and the Eskimo curlew teeters on the brink of oblivion, if it has not already disappeared. The woodcock's numbers have slumped and the whimbrel, or Hudsonian curlew, which once stopped by the scores of thousands in Nova Scotia to fatten up on berries for the fall migration, is seen now only in slender flocks. Knots, or large sandpipers, were abundant at Cape Breton stopovers before heavy hunting decimated them. Many other birds, like owls and hawks, live like thin shadows of former populations.

Drastic changes in the distribution of creatures have occurred. The salmon have gone from many rivers and small streams. The sturgeon survives in small numbers. Clams, oysters and lobsters have disappeared from many parts where once they were common. All the larger animals, caribou, moose, lynx, bobcats, porcupines, are severely restricted and live in fractions of their former numbers.

Men have everywhere upset local ecologies by importing, knowingly or unwittingly, harmful creatures from other areas. The European sawfly, which landed on North American shores some time in the late 19th century, was discovered attacking two thousand square miles of spruce in the Gaspé in 1930. Like the budworm, the sawfly attacks needled foliage, eventually killing the tree by the sheer density of numbers of its larvae. It found eastern Canada a haven. Nothing attacked it while its larvae gobbled away and when it dropped to the forest floor to pupate, transform into a fly, and take to the air again, forest mice and shrews could not eat enough of them to control the plague.

The presence of man, as an ecological dominant, automatically ensured that many millions of creatures would be destroyed in order to permit exploitation of the environment. As a forester, man could not tolerate the spruce budworm and he was bound to destroy any insect which, in two outbreaks alone in New Brunswick, ruined enough timber to encircle the earth with a two-foot-thick wall of wood as high as a 12-storey building.

In his efforts to control, to exploit, and to otherwise manipulate the environment, man has made many radical alterations to the plant life of the region. Prince Edward Island, once dense forest, is now open farmland with scattered woodlots. The Avalon peninsula in Newfoundland is now mostly barren where once it was largely forested. Most of the shores of Newfoundland have lost their tree cover because of human habitation. Through repeated firing the "mix" of trees has changed. The fire-resistant trees, or those adapted to capitalize on fire, have increased. Commercially valuable trees have disappeared from many areas; for example, the white pine from Nova Scotia.

There have been other, less outwardly dramatic, geographical changes. The steady leaching of fertility from cleared forest land has been especially damaging, with its twin corollaries of floods in spring and lowered streams and rivers in summer. Animal populations may recover but the lost fertility is gone for hundreds of years. So much for generalizations; the specifics show the impact of man on the region.

Writing of a 1610 visit to Newfoundland, Sir Richard Whitbourne said, "whereupon we sailed from thence and came to Trinity Harbour in Newfoundland where we killed a great store of fish, deere, beares, beavers, seales, otters and suchlike with an abundance of sea fowle, and so returning to England we arrived safe at Southampton." Sir Richard's "great store" of animals in Newfoundland sounds like a fairy tale today.

Nicholas Denys, born in Tours in 1598, found salmon "six feet in length" in a small river north of Nepisiguit, and saw even bigger sturgeons disporting themselves in the tide. The sturgeon coped fairly well with man's occupancy for a couple of hundred years. The fish was still abundant enough in the St. John River in the 19th century when it broke down fish nets during its spawning migrations. Many early travellers were astonished to see great numbers of sturgeon basking in the Oromocto Shallows about seventy miles off the New Brunswick shore, and hurling themselves out of the water, perhaps in an attempt to rip lamprey eels off their bellies. Today, the sturgeon is a victim of pollution, heavy fishing and river dams. It is rare, and rarely six feet long.

The ancient salmon fishery on the Miramichi River demonstrates the extent of the early destruction of wildlife. The first British settler was William Davidson from Scotland. He settled on the banks of the river in 1764, and for years he caught between three hundred and four hundred tons of salmon annually. Another fisherman, George Powell, reported in 1798 that he once caught seven hundred salmon in a single twenty-four hour period.

The abundance of the salmon on the Restigouche was scarcely less impressive. John Duncan, a farmer who lived near Campbellton in the 18th century, reported that eleven salmon averaged a barrel, or two hundred pounds, of fish. The largest salmon he saw weighed sixty pounds, although even this was a long way from Denys' six-foot leviathans. By 1848, however, the fish were down to seventeen to the barrel, and between 1828 and 1848, the catch on the river declined from three thousand barrels to three hundred.

In the Petitcodiac River, the salmon survived the settlement of Acadian French from Nova Scotia in 1720. They surmounted the erection of the first few dams and lumber mill weirs. But in 1848, Moses Perley watched about thirty-five "haymakers making war upon a few salmon which had reached a pool." He saw destruction of salmon everywhere on the river, with "no regard . . . paid to season." About two-thirds of the middle and upper reaches of the Petitcodiac were heavily dammed for lumbering but perhaps this was less damaging than the cutting of the trees. Today, hundreds of Atlantic shore rivers and streams are too shallow to permit salmon runs. Even when the salmon do manage to dig their nests in shallow water, heat often kills the hatching fish. The parr salmon can be seen seeking tiny areas where cooler spring seepages enter the rivers.

Moses Perley was impressed by the extremely large bass caught in the Miramichi and warned that hunting pressure would soon wipe them out. The fish gathered in large shoals, resting just underneath the surface of the ice, he noted, and it was a simple matter for fishermen to cut a hole in the ice, lower a bagnet, and haul up *all* the bass. The fish were caught through the ice on the Richibucto River too, then piled like stacks of firewood. Often, the thaw came before men could sled the great catches away. Today, only moderate numbers of bass are found in the Miramichi and Richibucto rivers.

A gannet and its mate prepare for nesting.

Gannets of Bonaventure

One of the largest and most accessible colonies of gannets is on Bonaventure Island. The island, with over 1300 nests, has recently been made a sanctuary for these birds. The gannet is a large seabird, almost the size of a goose, and about twice the size of the herring gull. Flocks of birds will hover over a school of fish, pick out a victim, then drop head first, like an arrow, from up to a hundred feet in the air. Air sacs located beneath the skin help cushion the blow on impact.

◄ *The high cliffs of Bonaventure Island glisten with nesting and soaring gannets in summer.*

A gannet collects sticks and other debris which is to be used as nesting material.

Both sexes help to incubate the single, whitish egg.

Gannets, awkward and clumsy on land, come ashore only during the breeding season, spending most of the year feeding and sleeping at sea. In spring, numbers of gannets often cover the cliffs, making ready their nesting territories. Both male and female build the nest, incubate the egg, and care for the young, but the parents desert the young bird after 12 weeks. It may spend a week or so at the nest site, then falls or glides from the cliffs to the water, where it quickly learns to fish for itself. These tame, fearless birds have few natural enemies. In the 19th century, fishermen reduced the gannets on Bonaventure to a danger point, slaughtering the birds to use as fish bait.

Adults and greyish juveniles in the gannetry.▶
The red markings are for research purposes.

There is evidence to suggest that gannets, like gulls, are very sensitive to DDT, which may affect their reproduction and cause eggs with thin, fragile shells.

Hunting pressure in the Atlantic region was frequently a reflection of man's fight for survival and the wildlife often strenuously resisted the hunting, none more so than the great auk. This flightless seabird was about the size of a goose, and its fat body made it valuable to all hunters. It only came to land to breed. When men arrived in the region, the great auk occupied many breeding islands but it was most numerous on Funk Island. Jacques Cartier, landing there in 1534, saw thousands of the big birds. After Cartier came the hunting fishermen, seeking fresh meat and eggs before or after transatlantic voyages.

At first, the men merely butchered the birds ready for salting and loaded a few thousand eggs into barrels and sailed away. But it was soon discovered that the great auk was extremely fat, so much so that its hunters could fuel their fat-rendering cauldrons with the bodies of the great auks themselves. They built stone pens to hold the waiting victims and may even have broken the legs of the birds to stop them escaping before tossing them alive into the cauldrons. Despite this, the great auk lasted through the 18th century. It was scarce, however, at the beginning of the 19th century, and the last one is believed to have been killed in the eastern Atlantic in 1844.

Funk Island is a kind of historical monument to this destruction of seabird life. Cartier saw large numbers of gannets on the island. When a Peter Stuvitz visited the island in 1841, the gannets had gone. Elsewhere in the Atlantic region, the gannet suffered from the fishermen's need for bait. When John James Audubon visited Bird Rock in the Gulf of Saint Lawrence in 1833, he thought the rock was covered with snow. The "snow" was gannets, perhaps a quarter of a million of them, nesting on every available square foot of the bleak rock. But, as bait supplies diminished elsewhere, the fishermen turned to Bird Rock.

Arthur Cleveland Bent, a 19th century ornithologist, noted that there were about forty fishing boats dependant on the gannets for bait, and that up to one hundred thousand birds were taken off the rock annually. In 1860, about 150,000 birds were left. In 1887, after a lighthouse was built, there were ten thousand birds but by 1939 only about one thousand remained.

The murres of Funk Island provide another saga in the destruction of wildlife. There are no reports of their early abundance on the island, but after the extinction of the great auk, they seem to have built up a big colony. The hunt for murres, however, turned out to be scarcely less enthusiastic than for the great auk. Fishermen used short flat paddles to smash down on the heads of the nesting murres (the birds are "standfasts" and will not retreat from the nest when menaced). Men even camped on the island, systematically slaughtering tens of thousands of the densely-packed birds.

Some old Newfoundland fishermen who are still alive can remember when the island was surrounded by as many as twenty schooners carrying a total of about four hundred men. Each man would need one murre a day to sustain him during his month or so on the Labrador coast. In the late 19th century, when Newfoundland exploitation of the Labrador was at its height, upwards of one hundred schooners would be fishing in the north, and at least half of them stopped at Funk Island. In those days, the annual kill of murres on Funk Island was between forty and fifty thousand.

Duck slaughter was—and still is—a feature of the Atlantic region. The white-winged scoters which prowled the Quebec shore searching for small black mussels and fish were also so fond of herring spawn that hunters could fire a dozen shots into a feeding flock before it took off. Napoléon Comeau, a redoubtable hunter in any age, killed thousands of them by arranging canoes along the shore in such a way that the craft deflected the flying birds towards a gunning boat. "I have seen small bunches of birds completely wiped out in a round like this," Comeau observed. There was another, and cheaper, way to kill them. In July, when the birds were moulting, Indians and whites drove among the temporarily flightless birds in boats, shouting, firing shotguns and roiling the water with paddles. The ducks dived again and again until they drowned. The advent of the breech-loader and the pump gun, however, was finally too much for the ducks. As Comeau himself noted sadly, "their numbers decreased or the birds have gone to other localities."

The willow ptarmigans once formed vast flocks along the south shore of Quebec in the 19th and early 20th centuries. They were hunted vigorously by every "man, woman and boy able to handle a gun," as one observer put it. Comeau checked the ptarmigan kill. Between Mingan and Godbout which contains about 175 miles of coastline, more than 30,000 birds were killed from 1895 to 1904. In 1885, 60,000 were slain during a particularly heavy migration.

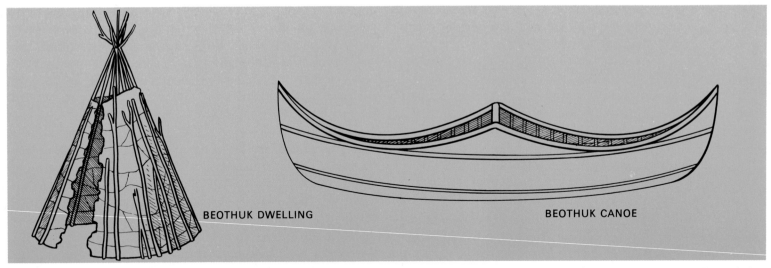

BEOTHUK DWELLING

BEOTHUK CANOE

Pictured above are a summer home and fishing boat used by Beothuk Indians who long ago lived in Newfoundland and, according to legend, they fought the Norsemen. Two and a half centuries ago, the French offered a reward for every Beothuk scalp, ending in total extinction of the tribe.

In some areas birds were hunted for food but in other places they were slaughtered merely to satisfy the urge to kill. In 1875, Comeau shot one thousand murres for the best of their feathers, and once he brought down a score of terns with one shot, just for fun. All the early hunters were fascinated by the fact that scores, sometimes hundreds of birds could be killed with one shot. In Newfoundland, on the east coast, where eider ducks cluster on open inshore patches of water in winter, hunters used blunderbusses, long toms and even cannons to get duck meat. Kills of three and four hundred birds in one broadside were not at all uncommon.

The hunting pressure on wildlife was often indiscriminate. Comeau knew one hunter who caught one hundred snowy owls, several dozen grey and long-eared owls, many gyrfalcons, duckhawks, and jays one winter by setting light traps mounted on poles. Comeau noted that five traps yielded him one thousand pounds of meat. All hawks and eagles were fair game. Comeau killed three golden eagles in a morning. The largest had a wingspan of seven feet. He killed half a dozen bald eagles with a stick when they were unable to fly because they were so gorged on salmon flesh.

Comeau's kill lists are depressing, certainly, but they do indicate the original abundance of birds and mammals. He shot fifty otters in one season, along with sixty-nine lynx. He calculated that between five and six thousand porcupines were killed each year in his hunting area.

Legend has it that the Beothuk Indians of Newfoundland kept tame wolves as pets but no white man ever thought of a wolf as anything but a creature to be shot. In the 1830's, a government bounty of five pounds a head ensured their extinction. The last wolf went under a hunter's gun at Gaff Topsails in 1911. The Beothuks did not manage any better and they were shot or starved out by the redoubtable Newfoundland hunters by the early 19th century.

The whales of the Atlantic shore were decimated in the 18th and 19th centuries, mostly by Americans. They travelled in large schooners with crews of up to ten men, ranging deep into the Arctic in search of their prey. There is no record of the early abundance of these animals but when populations began to make a hesitating comeback at the turn of the century, hunting resumed in 1902. In 1904, men killed 1,275 whales. A scant ten years later, the whale resurgence was ended when catches slumped to 160. The whales were let alone for a while, then they were hit again after a complete hunting rest during World War II. In ten years after the war, 3,000 sperm, blue, sei and humpback whales were killed.

Whales, as totally oceanic mammals, can withstand this kind of hunting pressure but the walrus is not so flexible. It has to come ashore to breed, which ensured its annihilation in the Atlantic shore region. By the late 16th century, the hunting of walruses, or sea-cows, as they were called, was in full swing. The first British walrus expedition, under the command of Captain Richard Strang in the seventy-ton ship *Marigold*, left Falmouth in 1593. The British were warlike about the oil and ivory bounty of the walrus hunt and were likely to attack any European ship they found laden with walrus skins and tusks.

In the middle of the 18th century, a gentleman called Gridley, a resident of the Magdalen Islands, sent his men to a walrus breeding island where they prevented the big animals from landing. The strategy was to force the animals to land on another island, closer to Mr. Gridley's walrus-processing machinery. The hunting of walrus was ruined, finally, by greed. A British official wrote to Lord Hillsborough in 1770 that ". . . the inhabitants of this island, who had endeavoured to carry it (the fishery) on for some time past and fearing by that means the fishery might be rendered useless to all parties, if not entirely ruined, I have, by the advice of His Majesty's Council, passed an Act for the better regulation of it. . . ." It was too late, however. The walrus was soon gone.

Harp seals which breed on pack ice were not so easily exterminated. The seal hunt began in earnest around 1750 and by the second half of the 19th century, catches were down to about 500,000 seals a year from a high of a million or more. The catch was finally stabilized at about 150,000 young seals in the 20th century. Recently, this stability has been upset by increased hunting pressures. The Norwegians, who were kicked out of the White Sea sealing grounds by the Russians in 1946, immediately headed for the Canadian Atlantic region to hunt seals there. Since the war, a steady decline in the seal host has occurred, as the hunt goes on.

The caribou of Newfoundland, surprisingly, has withstood the hunting pressure of several centuries. Early in this century many people were pessimistic about the caribou's chances against the hunter. Said *Forest and Stream* editorially, "Caribou have long been most wastefully slaughtered in Newfoundland, and last winter it was a common sight to see carcasses piled up in front of business places of local auctioneers, and the veni-son sold all winter for a few cents a pound. Not many years ago, a man sold a hundred carcasses to French fishermen for fish bait, and in some years more animals have been killed than could be eaten, so that the carcasses had to be thrown into the sea."

P. T. McGrath, an American observer, watched in astonishment as the Newfoundlanders hunted the caribou laden with barrels of salt to attract the animals into suitable groups and heavy artillery to blast them down as they began licking.

"They ambush themselves along a promising 'lead' or deer track," McGrath wrote, "armed with long six-foot muzzle-loading sealing guns, which they charge with about 'eight fingers' of coarse gunpowder and 'slugs' of lead, fragments of iron and bits of rusty nails, whichever they may have. They fire point blank into a herd of caribou as it passes, and being usually good shots, contrive to kill almost anything they aim at, or wound it so badly with those dreadful missiles that it soon collapses."

Today, the destruction of wildlife is more likely to be indirect. Pollution, great or small, affects every major river in the Maritime region. New Brunswick's most southern river, the St. Croix, is polluted by a pulp mill in Maine which discharges the equivalent outflow of sewage of 500,000 people. The pollution is so bad in mid-summer that observers have seen eels—just about the toughest of all marine creatures—crawling dazed out of the water and dying on the banks of the poisoned river. The St. John River is polluted by one large mill 300 miles from its mouth and the chemical effects do not taper off until Fredericton. There is a dam at Fredericton, anyway, which has destroyed the anadromous fish run.

One big pulp and paper mill at the mouth of the Miramichi is not quite enough to stop the salmon run, but another mill on the other side of the river would destroy the richest salmon river on earth. Already, on one tributary of the Miramichi system, the water is so badly polluted from effluents from a mine that nothing lives in it.

The hunter, the forester, the industrialist, and, finally, the suburbanite, all compete with animals and plants for a share of the living space. In this respect the Atlantic region resembles every other region where men are settled. The question for the future of the Atlantic shore is: Can the wealth of the region, what's left of it, be conserved, and if so, how?

17 REPAIRING THE DAMAGE

To repair the damage done by man's occupation of the Atlantic region, a great fact-finding program is now underway which involves every discipline of the life sciences. The scientists are trying to find out why creatures and plants live where, and in what numbers. They are taking the biological process apart cell by cell. At least one man has equipped birds—snipe—with two-way radios to report their positions to him constantly. Another has used crossbows to tag tuna and follow their movements. Many scientists are skin-diving in pursuit of knowledge and observational submarines will soon join helicopters as information-gathering vehicles. Most important, the fact-finding is co-operative, involving scientists from the six universities in the area, the Fisheries Research Board, the Agriculture Department, the Federal wildlife scientists and many private groups, including sportsmen's clubs and bird-watchers.

From such knowledge will come the capacity to repair damage done, and even to improve on natural process. The manipulation of environment and the conservation of natural resources is not, of course, a new idea. Ancient records of civilization show that men have always juggled with the ingredients of their environments, importing animals and plants from China, or cats from Egypt, and transplanting trees from Lebanon to Assyria. Several hundred species of plants and animals have been forcibly transported from America to Europe, and vice versa, but such juggling was done without any regard for the biological consequences. Many of the "improvements" have turned out to be disasters—witness the sparrows and starlings and rabbits exported from Europe which overran their new territories, or the American grey squirrel and nutria exported from the U.S., which did the same.

The Atlantic region furnishes an excellent case history of such uninformed juggling. A French chocolate millionaire, Henri Menier, bought Anticosti Island in 1895 for $125,000, hoping to establish a wildlife paradise for hunters on the island. Menier was not deterred by the fact that Anticosti was a bad deal from a hunter's point of view. It had only five native mammals: the deermouse, the eastern black bear, the Labrador red fox, the pine marten, and the eastern Canada otter—hardly exciting targets for French guns. Menier tried to diversify the game. He imported about fifty beaver which flourished. He followed with white-tailed deer, and they were so successful that today the island's deer population has hit the three-to-four-hundred-thousand mark. Then he tried bison but the experiment failed. Around the turn of the century, he brought in moose, and by the 1950's Anticosti had a moose herd of about 250 animals. He liberated six hundred snowshoe hares during the winter of 1902-3, and they have flourished (which must have been a great boon to the pine martens who were able, presumably, to get off the rather dull diet of deermice). Menier brought in fishers which did not make it, and mink which flourished for a while before dying out. He imported wapiti but they became so abundant and dangerous they had to be shot out. The wapiti cows of peaceable disposition remained on, walking up and down the streets of the island's biggest town, Port Menier, until the fall of 1936 when they were killed. The French millionaire's last effort at juggling with the ecology of Anticosti was to import reindeer but this effort, surprisingly, was a failure.

Menier's hit-or-miss tampering with nature illuminates an important point which is not lost on contemporary biologists: when a creature is well-fitted into its ecological niche, it is very difficult to dislodge, a thesis illustrated by the lobster's survival into the 20th century. Although it was always known as a delicacy in the Atlantic region, earnest fishing for it did not begin until 1850. From 1870, lobster quite suddenly became cheap meat for everyone. By 1885, the Atlantic lobster catch rocketed to one hundred million pounds. This intense fishing skimmed off the mature, heavily egg-bearing lobsters in the area, and the catches dropped quickly to about twenty million pounds where they have stayed, more or less stable, until the present day.

Man and lobster have come to an ecological "agreement," and the lobster crop seems ensured for the future. More or less the same can be said for the clam, the oyster, the caribou, the moose, the snipe, the woodcock, the herring, the codfish, shrimp, ducks and other seabirds as well as the salmon and the lumber- and pulp-producing forests.

Four hundred years of human occupation have created a new ecological system, with man as the dominant influence. In those four centuries, man has been brought to the understanding that he can, roughly speaking, catch one million tons of codfish, 200,000 tons of herring, 50,000 tons of redfish, and chop down 100,000 tons of lumber and pulpwood a year without reducing the original resource. He can shoot 100,000 ducks, catch 68,000 salmon, and kill 1500 snipe and woodcock and 100,000 murres. He can eat five million pounds of oysters, twenty million pounds of lobsters, and thirty-two million pounds of scallops and clams and this will not affect future populations. He can shoot 1500 caribou and 700 moose, and gun down scores of thousands of rabbits, squirrels, woodchucks, foxes and ptarmigans without upsetting the existing ecology.

In the mid-20th century, it is possible to pause, then, and examine the ecological status of the Atlantic region; to measure the quality of interaction between man and his environment. The disasters and damage outlined in the previous chapter are indisputable but there are many balancing factors. It is true that heavy fishing has cut down the size, and probably the quantities, of most commercial fishing stocks, but *all* these stocks are younger, more dynamic and, as one biologist put it, "they taste better." There are no more forty-pound lobsters, but the two-pounders are more succulent, and probably more numerous.

The great auk is extinct but the remaining seabirds are increasing, some of them rapidly. Since the 1930's, the murres of Funk Island have increased from about one thousand to more than one million. The gannets at Baccalieu, Bird Rock, Bonaventure and Cape St. Mary's are all increasing. Puffins and cormorants are increasing both their numbers and their ranges.

Although some mammals and shorebirds are rare today compared with yesterday's abundance, none is in immediate danger of extinction. For shorebirds like the Hudsonian and Eskimo curlews, the reasons for their rarity are probably to be found beyond the Atlantic region anyway. It is true that forests have been cut and burned ceaselessly since white men settled, but Nova Scotia and New Brunswick are expanding their forest-land as thousands of marginal farms are abandoned, and improved forestry methods are adopted. This expansion is

A lobster can shed its old shell in just twenty minutes. After moulting ▶ *the lobster absorbs sea-water and swells, increasing its weight by fifty per cent. The new shell hardens as the lobster feeds.*

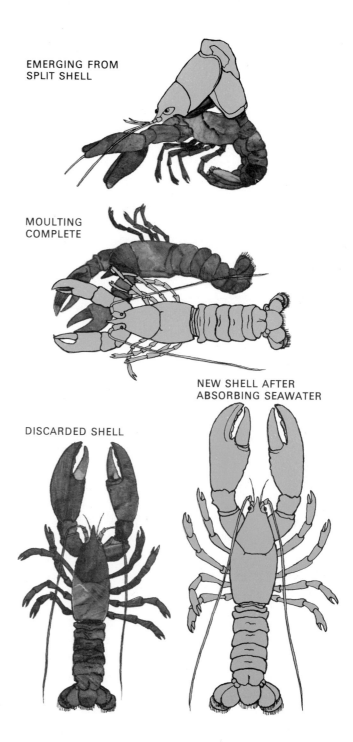

EMERGING FROM
SPLIT SHELL

MOULTING
COMPLETE

NEW SHELL AFTER
ABSORBING SEAWATER

DISCARDED SHELL

The great auk has long been extinct and the osprey is in danger. Weak-shelled eggs and fewer young seem connected with pesticides.

creating new habitats for all kinds of animals from deer to deermice. The harp seals, over-exploited for two hundred years, and with their numbers declining, have been reprieved. Tough new international regulations now control the catches to match the capacity of the surviving seals to breed. The Beothuks and the walruses are gone forever, alas, but it is unlikely that they would have held their places in the Atlantic region, even without hunting. Neither population felt comfortable with the coming of Caucasian man.

The old days of killing for the sake of killing have pretty much gone. There are no Napoléon Comeaus today. Instead, there are thousands of conservation-minded people who belong to various bird-watching clubs, Audubon Societies, and hunting groups. Instead of U.S.-Canadian quarrels over herring fishing at Grand Manan, there is the International Commission of North Atlantic Fisheries to decide net mesh sizes, the degree of exploitation, and the future of fishing for the area.

However, it is less the desire to conserve than the need to know which is important today. Snipe flit in the twilight sending out radio messages, and one day such exhaustive research on their habits will fit into a mosaic of knowledge involving the total Maritime ecosystem at work. Already, men know five years in advance if the haddock fishing will be good; if the salmon numbers will slump or boom. They are grappling with the macromanipulations of environments, encouraging some populations, discouraging others, controlling diseases, and importing aliens to fill empty niches in environments. The man-nature relationship is no longer exemplified by the primeval, unspoiled wilderness that so many nature-lovers and conservationists yearn for. Instead, it is man-in-control of nature. A Newfoundland ecologist and biologist, A. T. Bergerud, has expressed the concept of "crops" of wild animals. "Wildlife management," he has said, "is the science of making the land produce sustained crops of wildlife."

Sustained crops cannot be harvested sensibly, however, until the life histories of the "crops" are known. Where, for instance, do the tuna come from? S. N. Tibbo, a scientist of St. Andrews, New Brunswick, spent several summers using a bow and arrow device to shoot tags into the hides of tuna. His assistant developed a method of branding sharks like cattle in order to trace their migrations. Cod are easily tagged, and so are salmon. Radio telemetry of birds promises to go beyond following them around their breeding grounds. Eventually, migrating birds will carry radios that would be activated by a satellite hovering over the Atlantic region.

Thousands of birds would report their positions every hour to the satellite which would then transmit the information to a computer on earth.

Ignorance of life cycles makes any sort of sensible regulation or exploitation of wild populations impossible. In the 1870's, a population explosion of salmon spread through most of the Atlantic region. This was followed in the 1880's by an extraordinary salmon slump. Oddly, the greatest declines in populations occurred, as one scientist put it, "in rivers which are neither obstructed by mill dams nor afflicted with sawdust nor poachers to any extent."

The salmon feast-and-famine passed into history, but the cyclical fluctuation of the fish in nine-year phases continued. It was variously attributed to overfishing, bad fishing habits, poachers, disease. In the 20th century, however, it was observed that great predators of salmon smolts were two water birds, the belted kingfisher and the American merganser. Might these birds influence the numbers of adult salmon? Subsequently, research demonstrated that when rivers were at their normal heights, few young salmon were caught because the birds found it easier to catch trout swimming close to the surface. But in periods of low water, when the rivers were clear, the two water birds cut down the numbers of salmon which made their run to the sea. They annihilated seagoing salmon in 1880-81, in 1919-20, and in 1928. The solution was simple. Shoot out the mergansers and kingfishers. A normal merganser population in a good salmon stream is about ten birds for every fifteen miles of stream. By cutting the mergansers down to one bird for every fifteen miles, the salmon thrived in all years, drought included.

Merganser-control, however, is only one segment of the effort to manipulate salmon. Another method is to boost populations artificially. Dr. A. G. Huntsman of New Brunswick planted 200,000 underyearling salmon in the North River. He got a yield of 4500 smolts. The following year he planted 40,000 underyearlings and got almost the same return of smolts as from the first planting. Obviously, there was a precise limit to the capacity of the environment to support additional numbers. Since these experiments, it has been found that the average Atlantic stream can produce about five to six smolts for every one hundred square yards (with kingfisher and merganser control). Only about eight per cent of smolts survive the sea-trip, and return to the river of their birth. Commercial and sporting fishermen get about twenty-five per cent of all the adult salmon stock each year.

Such knowledge is a way station on the route to future control. There are many possibilities for improving salmon populations, including dumping truckloads of stones into the open bottoms of streams to increase the number of hiding places for young parr, a device that is also being used experimentally in the southern Gulf of Saint Lawrence to create new populations of lobsters. The flow patterns of streams can be altered if they are unfavourable to salmon survival. Adding, or eliminating trees at streamside may help the salmon. One scientist has already constructed artificial spawning beds in the Moser River in Nova Scotia. The salmon used the beds eagerly. Others have experimented with creating artificial freshets to attract salmon into rivers. It is obvious that as knowledge of the biology of any living thing increases, the possibilities for such manipulation also increase.

Because men everywhere in the Atlantic region are a vital part of the ecological picture, they must, in order to secure control, assume the role of predator if natural predation is not working out to their benefit. Shooting mergansers is an easy and safe case in point. But to achieve larger results, it may be necessary to take some risks, at least until more subtle forms of control are developed. The millions of songbirds which died in New Brunswick forests under the first DDT attacks were part of the cost of saving a valuable timber crop. After the early disasters, two million acres were sprayed at half-strength. This did much less harm to the young salmon and aquatic invertebrates and did fairly well in quelling the budworm. New chemicals have entered the picture which are not residual in animal bodies, or in the earth. The Green River Project, a co-operative effort of Federal, provincial and private forestry people, has already isolated the causes of the budworm attacks — which involves large areas of mature-to-decadent forests — and has coordinated efforts to harvest mature trees before the budworm strikes. Eventually, the budworm may be tackled with some form of biotic control.

Already, biotic control has worked on other pests. In 1936, a virus disease was discovered in the laboratory which attacked sawflies, then ravaging New Brunswick and Gaspé forests. The virus was bred and released. Within three years, it had smashed 99 per cent of the sawfly larvae in New Brunswick. Within seven years, the outbreak was ended, without spraying, unnecessary

The spruce budworm is a serious pest in conifer forests. Young caterpillars overwinter beneath bark (1) and in spring they feed voraciously on buds and new growth (2) Pupation takes place during the early summer (3) and adults emerge and lay eggs in late summer (4).

death, recrimination or, indeed, much expense.

Biotic control suggests an almost infinite scope for controlling wild populations. Although control of disease is still in its infancy, some surprising successes have been achieved. When an epidemic disease hit the oysters of New Brunswick and Nova Scotia in 1954-55, the Federal Department of Fisheries immediately restocked the depleted beds with immunized oysters from Prince Edward Island. The Prince Edward Island oysters, first hit by the disease in 1915 in Malpeque Bay, had then suffered 90 per cent mortality. The surviving ten per cent took twenty years to rebuild the Malpeque populations. By reseeding with these immune oysters, the fisheries people cut in half the recovery period of the Nova Scotia and New Brunswick stocks.

More recently, a Prince Edward Island oyster researcher, R. A. Drinnan, has perfected a method of spawning oysters artificially, and early, and so releasing the larvae into the southern gulf waters weeks ahead of the wild oyster larvae. In one year, Drinnan has found, his artificially-bred oysters can make as much growth as a two-year-old wild oyster.

No one knows what causes the oyster epidemics, although a virus is the logical suspect. If it were ever isolated, it might be possible to artificially immunize the oysters by some kind of mass oceanic inoculation. Certainly some diseases are destructive enough to make this kind of research worthwhile. Lobsters, for instance, suffer from a bacteria which eats through their shells and into the soft body parts. In addition, they suffer from a blood disease which upsets the clotting capacity and affects respiration.

In the 1930's, when a virus disease hit the eelgrass meadows of the Atlantic shores, it not only wiped out most of the eelgrass but it also eliminated a vast series of habitats for countless marine creatures, including oysters. Moreover, it wiped out the main source of food used by brant geese during migration and within a couple of years, the brant were decimated.

Although such disasters hurt only the sentimental and aesthetic side of man's nature, other diseases hurt his pocketbook. It is these that he will seek to control first. In the late spring and early summer of 1954, an epidemic disease hit the herring of the Gulf of Saint Lawrence. The epidemic was caused by a fungus, a pathogen causing a systemic infection which concentrated in the heart. Billions of herring died. More than half the entire gulf stocks died, and the effects of the epidemic spread throughout the Atlantic region. Fishing catches were slashed by more than 20,000 tons. The disease raged on through 1956, with dazed and dying herring visible everywhere on sea and along shorelines.

Eventually, the disease hit home so disastrously in the Newfoundland area that scientists believe it altered the spawning habits of local stocks. From spring spawners only, the herring changed to spawners in almost every month of the year as a way to recover old population levels. As a final blow, the disease also upset the normal migration patterns and the general distribution of the fish. The $9,000,000 loss to the herring industry was a reminder that the high costs of research into disease control might be rapidly recovered by one successful prevention of an epidemic.

Yet disease control can do little to improve the productivity of environments. Importing alien animals can, although the method may be dangerous if done without exhaustive biological study of the consequences. The residents of Grand Manan imported a pair of moose to the island in the 19th century and within a few years were harvesting an annual yield of moose meat between four and five tons.

Importing animals into the Atlantic region has been a feature of environmental manipulation. Not enough time has passed since the withdrawal of the ice for all life to have had its chance to colonize. Before 1878, no moose lived on Newfoundland, but the six animals imported between 1878 and 1904 soon grew into a big herd. From 1878 to the late 1950's, about 60,000 animals were shot. Today, about five thousand a year are killed.

There are, of course, penalties for this kind of thing. Local biologists must balance the moose populations against the capacity of balsam fir to regenerate under the influence of moose grazing. Too many moose kill entire forests of the future. The problem of control is complicated by the fact that the moose has no enemies except men with rifles. Biologists must therefore use the riflemen as though they are the predators. When the moose become too abundant, the herd must be thinned. Newfoundland hunters may, in moose-plentiful times, get free accommodation where moose are grazing heavily, free ferry boats to get them across lakes, and spotter planes to guide them to their prey.

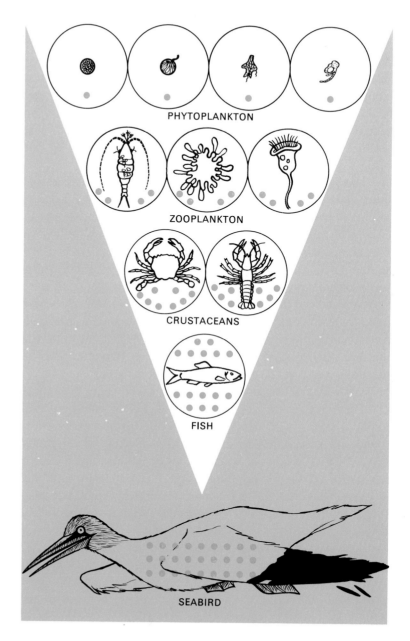

The end of the line

To gain a pound, a seabird must consume the equivalent of ten thousand pounds of phytoplankton. Thus a poison stored by the plankton would be multiplied many times over by the time the bird ate the fish that ate the crab, etc. Poisons accumulate in the tissue and can kill the bird or can affect the formation of eggs.

PHYTOPLANKTON

ZOOPLANKTON

CRUSTACEANS

FISH

SEABIRD

One of the most successful wildlife management programmes in Newfoundland involves the willow ptarmigan. The ptarmigan never made it to Newfoundland after the withdrawal of the ice (and why not is a puzzle), but after its introduction from Labrador by man, it thrived even though its mortality rate is between seventy and eighty per cent annually. Hunters can take out up to forty percent of an entire population each year without diminishing that population for the next year by one bird.

The Newfoundland biologist, A. T. Bergerud, has said that other niches in Newfoundland environments might be filled with imported creatures. The spruce grouse, for instance, should be able to fit into a corner not presently exploited by the willow ptarmigan. It may not have much sporting value since it is a skulking species, but it would give emergency food to other forms of life, and would populate the otherwise almost birdless spruce forests of the island. The red squirrel is another possible immigrant. It would contribute food for other animals and pelts for human hunters. In particular, it would help to feed the pine martens. Sharp-tailed grouse could survive, Bergerud feels, in the transition zone between the dense forests and the treeless barrens. They are a sporting bird and make excellent eating.

There are possibilities for many kinds of environmental manipulation, one of which is a small pilot project of the Newfoundland government to test whether muskeg, the peatland that covers thousands of square miles of the northland, can be made productive. Already, the muck land, useless for anything in its raw state, has grown bumper crops of vegetables and first-rate grass, but at a cost still too high to make reclamation worthwhile.

The heart of Newfoundland may one day flower with crops, but a more immediate environmental proposal is the Passamaquoddy Power Project which has been promulgated for twenty years as a joint U.S.-Canadian venture along the lines of the Saint Lawrence Seaway. The project would join a series of islands across Passamaquoddy Bay with dams to create new sources of electric power when the Fundy tides rise and fall.

A Fisheries Research Board boat working in the Atlantic region. The ▶ high cost of research into disease control is rapidly recovered by prevention of epidemics that cause great losses in the fishing industry.

But the dams would wipe out most of the clams, destroy the haddock and decimate the pollack. Scallops would be boosted because their larvae would survive better in the contained area. There would be a population explosion of shipworms, which would become an "expensive pest" because the increased water temperatures would encourage their breeding and survival. The herring, however, would not be seriously inconvenienced because they would be able to get in and out of the bay through entry points in the dams.

Environmental manipulation is limited only by man's imagination. Another Newfoundland biologist, Leslie Tuck, has suggested the construction of concrete platforms on cliffs to give seabirds in crowded colonies more room to breed. He experimented on one island by clearing a small space of rocks and almost immediately 132 pairs of birds nested there.

The greatest environmental manipulation of all may come, in the end, out of the Atlantic forests. Foresters are on the threshold of creating new types of forests composed of trees that grow faster, straighter and more disease-free. Foresters are particularly impatient with Newfoundland's forests which grow slowly and recover reluctantly from natural or man-made disasters. They would like to see the present cover replaced with a hybrid tree that would have at least double the growth rate of present forests. Such new cover would, of course, create new ecological mixes of animals, insects and plants. Foresters, incidentally, are the only environment manipulators who can fiddle with genes and chromosomes, who can change or unite characteristics at will, but they are not likely to have a monopoly on this skill in the future.

It is, finally, the sea which is the most prolific and dynamic of all the Atlantic environments. The biology of nearly all sea creatures is dynamic enough to ensure their resistance to great hunting pressures. In the early 1960's, when the Russians moved into a new banks area and fished out 67,000 metric tons of herring in one year, there was consternation among local herring fishermen. But the scientists were undismayed. As one biologist said, "the herring has reproductive capacity far beyond man's present capability to deplete it."

Yields of fish from the Grand Banks and elsewhere go on despite periodic cries of doom by local fishermen. U.S. scientists have calculated that acre for acre, the sea is as productive as the land, but only about sixteen percent of its potential is being harvested. To secure the remaining eighty-four per cent is the objective of modern technology. About 10,000 tons of fish are lifted off the Grand Banks every day, a figure which may be increased tenfold in the future.

Methods for catching fish and processing them are constantly being refined. One such refinement, the Scottish development of the tern ramp trawler, was revolutionary. It allowed the entire netted catch to be winched up the stern ramp and dumped between decks where the fish were filleted, packed and frozen. A Russian mother ship on the banks today carries up to ten thousand tons of salted, dried, or pickled fish, and its attendant trawlers may be as big as large freighters.

Today's exploitation is, however, nothing to what is ahead. W. H. Johnson, of the Industrial Development Service of the Canadian Fisheries Department, has said that the trawler of the future may be equipped with a computer which, working with ASDIC to locate the fish, would direct the ship to the fish, alter the winches to set the gear at the right depth, adjust the ship's speed to coincide with the school, calculate the tension on the hawsers when the net was full, and haul it up automatically. The crew could be asleep.

In recent years, small, fast observation submarines have been developed on both sides of the Atlantic. These vessels will be used one day, it is theorized, to round up schools of fish like cattle or sheep, and drive them into the nets of prowling trawlers. U.S. scientists have already built various vehicles for fish-watching, fast enough to keep up with tuna and sharks and equipped with powerful lights for night work.

It is on this futuristic note that a natural history of the Atlantic region of Canada should be ended. A great and diversified complex of current and tide, of offshore banks and oceanic littoral, of pasture and ploughland, of mountain and salmon river, of orchard and expansive tideland, has passed through the full cycle of recovery from the ice age and from its collision with civilization, and has emerged–damaged, to be sure–a monument to the vitality of nature. Men, in their ignorance, may continue to damage the earth but in the end, the Atlantic shore experience hopefully suggests, it is possible for them to live harmoniously in their environment without destroying the earth around them.

GEOLOGIC TIME SCALE

TIME	ERA	PERIOD	EPOCH	THE ASCENT OF LIFE:
	CENOZOIC	QUATERNARY	PLEISTOCENE	
		TERTIARY	PLIOCENE	
			MIOCENE	
			OLIGOCENE	
50			EOCENE	
			PALEOCENE	
100	MESOZOIC	CRETACEOUS	UPPER / LOWER	
150		JURASSIC	UPPER / MIDDLE / LOWER	
200		TRIASSIC	UPPER / MIDDLE / LOWER	
250	PALAEOZOIC	PERMIAN	UPPER / MIDDLE / LOWER	
300		PENNSYLVANIAN		
		MISSISSIPPIAN		
350		DEVONIAN	UPPER / MIDDLE / LOWER	
400		SILURIAN		
450		ORDOVICIAN	UPPER / MIDDLE / LOWER	
500 / 550		CAMBRIAN	UPPER / MIDDLE / LOWER	

MILLIONS OF YEARS

THE ASCENT OF LIFE: 1, *protozoan*; 2, *jellyfish*; 3, *crinoid*; 4, *cephalopod*; 5, *climatius*; 6, *shark*; 7, *brachiopod*; 8, *seed fern*; 9, *dimetrodon*; 10, *brontosaurus*; 11, *plesiosaur*; 12, *tyrannosaurus*; 13, *taeniolabis*; 14, *diatryma*; 15, *hyracotherium*; 16, *brontotherium*; 17, *oxydactylus*; 18, *pliohippus*; 19, *mastodon*; 20, *man*.

141

SHORT LIST OF ROCKS, PLANTS AND ANIMALS

The lists on the following pages have been compiled as a basic guide for amateur naturalists intending to explore the wealth of the natural history of the Atlantic Coast region. These selected summaries cannot possibly cover all species — there are many thousands of insects alone — but an attempt has been made to include the common life forms and the natural phenomena peculiar to this region. Readers should find it useful to study the lists touching on their sphere of interest, checking off items they have observed during field trips. Those wishing to extend their search will find an extensive Bibliography on pages 153-5, the references listed there contain more detailed information on many specific subjects.

ROCKS

MESOZOIC ERA

TRIASSIC PERIOD
Basalt
Sandstone
Conglomerate
Shale

PALAEOZOIC ERA

CARBONIFEROUS PERIOD
Limestone
Sandstone
Siltstone
Arkose
Gypsum
Shale
Conglomerate
DEVONIAN PERIOD
Limestone
Shale
Sandstone

Slate
Quartzite
Arkose
Volcanic tuff
SILURIAN PERIOD
Argillite
Quartzite
ORDOVICIAN PERIOD
Slate
Graywacke
Dolomite
Conglomerate
CAMBRIAN PERIOD
Limestone
Sandstone
Siltstone
Graywacke

PRECAMBRIAN ERA

Arkose
Marble
Argillite
Schist
Graywacke
Gneiss
Amphibolite

Breccia
Tuff

MINERALS

Actinolite
Agate
Albertite
Amethyst
Analcite
Andalusite
Anhydrite
Ankerite
Antimony
Apatite
Apophyllite
Argentite
Arsenopyrite
Azurite
Barite
Beryl
Bismuth
Bornite
Braunite
Calcite
Cassiterite
Celadonite

Celestite
Chabazite
Chalcedony
Chalcocite
Chalcopyrite
Chert
Chlorite
Copper
Covellite
Dacite
Danburite
Dolomite
Epidote
Epistilbite
Fluorite
Galena
Garnet
Gersdorffite
Glaucodot
Gmelinite
Goethite
Gold
Gyrolite
Halite
Hausmannite
Hematite

Heulandite
Jasper
Kermesite
Laumontite
Limonite
Magnetite
Malachite
Manganite
Marcasite
Mesolite
Molybdenite
Mordenite
Muscovite
Natrolite
Prehnite
Proustite
Psilomelane
Pyrite
Pyrolusite
Pyroxene
Quartz
Ramsdellite
Scheelite
Scolecite
Selenite
Serpentine
Siderite
Sillimanite
Sphalerite
Stannite
Staurolite
Stibnite
Stilbite
Tennantite
Tetrahedrite
Thomsonite
Tourmaline
Valentinite
Wolframite

VERTEBRATE FOSSILS
NOVA SCOTIA
TRIASSIC PERIOD
Rhynchosaurs
Procolophonid Cotylosaurs
Ornithosuchid Pseudosuchians

Aëtosaurid Pseudosuchians
Coelurosaurian Dinosaurs

INVERTEBRATE FOSSILS
(HORTON-WINDSOR DISTRICT)
CARBONIFEROUS PERIOD
Molluscs
Sanguinolites parvus
Edmondia rudis
Parallelidon hardingi
Leptodesma borealis
Schizodus fundiensis
Aviculopectin lyelli
Modiola dawsoni
Scaldia fletcheri
Murchisonia gypsea
Naticopsis howi
Orthoceras vindobonense
Arthropods
Cypridina acadia
Paraparchites gibbus
Phillipsia eichwaldi
Cyclus subcircularis

NEWFOUNDLAND (Bonavista)
CAMBRIAN PERIOD
Molluscs
Hyolithes princeps
Iphidea labradorica
Helenia bella
Obolella atlantica
Coleoloides typicales
Urotheca pervetus
Trilobites
Callavia broggeri
Paradoxides davides

PLANT FOSSILS
NOVA SCOTIA (Sydney)
UPPER CARBONIFEROUS PERIOD
Liverworts
Marchantites
Sphenopterids
Sphenopteris striata

Sphenopteris neuropteroides
Neuropterids
Neuropteris tenuifolia
Neuropteris flexuosa
Alethopterids
Alethopteris serli
Alethopteris valida
Pecopterids
Asterotheca miltoni
Equisitales
Calamites suckowi
Anonularia radiata
Lycopodiales
Lepidodendron lycopodioides
Lepidodendron dichotomum

PLANTS

MOSSES
Smooth fern-moss
Hylocomium splendens
Rough fern-moss
Thudium delicatulum
Schreber's moss
Pleurozium schreberi
Shaggy moss
Rhytidiadelphus triquetrus
White moss
Leucobryum glaucum
Broom-moss
Dicranum scoparium
Tree-trunk moss
Ulota crispa
Bank moss
Mnium hornum
Spoon-leaved peat-moss
Sphagnum magellanicum
Narrow-leaved peat-moss
Sphagnum capillaceum
Swamp moss
Aulacomnium palustre
Dragonhead moss
Brachythecium salebrosum
Red moss
Ceratodon purpureus
Hair-cap moss
Polytrichum commune
Wavy-leaved moss
Atrichum undulatum

Broad-leaved moss
Mnium cuspidatum
Velvet moss
Dicranella heteromalla
Nodding moss
Pohlia nutans
Rock moss
Grimmia apocarpa
Grey boulder moss
Hedwigia ciliata
Apple moss
Bartramia pomiformis
Four-toothed moss
Tetraphis pellucida
Curly-leaved moss
Drepanecladus uncinatus
Roadside moss
Ditrichum pusillum

PLANTS OF THE SALT MARSHES
Cat-tail
Typha latifolia
Spike-grass
Distichlis spicata

Reed
Phragymites communis

Seaside wild rye
Elymus virginicus
Salt-marsh grass
Spartina alterniflora
Salt reed-grass
Spartina cynosaroides
Salt-meadow grass
Spartina patens
Fresh water cord-grass
Spartina pectinata
Panic grass
Panicum longifolium
Sedge
Cyperus polystachyos
Chair-maker's rush
Scirpus americanus

Salt-marsh bulrush
Scirpus maritimus
Horned rush
Rhynchospora macrostachya
Black grass
Juncus gerardi
Soft rush
Juneus effusus
Blue-eyed grass
Sisyrinchium arenicola
Ladies-tresses
Spiranthes cernua
Seabeach knotweed
Polygonum glaucum
Coast blite
Chenopodium rubrum
Woody glasswort
Salicornia virginica
Samphire
Salicornia bigelovii
Sea-blite
Suaeda maritima
Sand spurrey
Spergularia marina
Sea milkwort
Glanx maritima
Sea lavender (Marsh Rosemary)
Limonium carolinianum
Seaside gerardia
Gerardia maritima
Early seaside plantain
Plantago juncoides
Slender-leaved goldenrod
Solidago tenuifolia
Salt-marsh aster
Aster tenuifolius
Groundsel-tree
Baccharis halimifolia
Salt-marsh fleabane
Pluchea purpurascens

PLANTS OF THE DUNES

Beach grass
Ammophila breviligulata
Bayberry
Myrica pensylvanica
Jointweed
Polygonella articulata
Seabeach orach
Atriplex arenaria
Seabeach sandwort
Arenaria peploides
Sea rocket
Cakile edentala

Beach plum
Prunus martima
Salt-spray rose
Rosa rugosa
Seaside spurge
Euphorbia polygonifolia
Poison Ivy
Rhus radicans
Poverty grass
Hudsonia tomentosa
Pinweed
Lechea maritima
Bearberry
Arctostaphylos uva-ursi
Sickle-leaved golden aster
Chrysopsis falcata
Seaside goldenrod
Solidago sempervirens
Cocklebur
Xanthium echinatum
Wormwood
Artemisia candata
Dusty miller
Artemisia stelleriana

SEASHORE PLANTS

Eel grass
Zostera marina
Sea lettuce
Ulva lactuca
Rockweed
Fucus vesiculosis

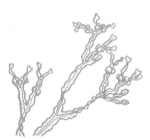

Green seaweed
Enteromorpha intestinalis
Ascophyllum nodosum
Kelp
Laminaria agardhii
Winged kelp
Alaria esculenta
Sea colander
Agarum cribrosum
Dulse
Rhodymenia palmata
Irish moss
Chondrus crispus

SEASIDE PLANTS

Soapwort
Saponaria officinalis
Shadbush
Amelanchier canadensis
Scotch broom
Cytisus scoparius
Scarlet pimpernel
Anagallis arvensis
Chicory
Cichorium intybus
Common evening primrose
Oenothera biennis
Queen Anne's lace
Daucus carota
Sumac
Rhus ghabra

WILD FLOWERS

Bog Solomon-plume
Smilacina trifolia
Twisted-stalk
Streptopus amplexifolius
Rosybells
Streptopus roseus
Catbrier
Smilax rotundifolia
Carrion-flower
Smilax herbacea
Goldstar-grass
Hypoxis hirsuta
Narrow-leaf lily
Iridaceae prismatica
Golden slipper orchid
Cypripedium parviflorum
Moccasin orchid
Cypripedium acaule

Tubercled rein-orchid
Habenaria flava
Purple fringe orchid
Habenaria fimbriata
Green-eyed ladies-tresses
Spiranthes gracilis
Checkered rattlesnake orchid
Goodyera tellelata
Green adder-mouth orchid
Malaxis unifolia
Fairy-slipper orchid
Calypso bulbosa
Five-leaf orchid
Osotria verticallata
Woodland Jack-in-the-pulpit
Arisaema triphyllum
Northern Jack-in-the-pulpit
Arisaema stewardsonii
Green dragon
Arisaema dracontium
Skunk cabbage
Symplocarpus foetidus

Wild calla
Calla palustris
Pink catchfly
Silene pennsylvanica
Pickerelweed
Pontederia cordata
Wood anemone
Anemone quinquefolia
Rock clematis
Clematis verticillaris
Marsh-marigold
Caltha palustris
Eastern columbine
Aquilegia canadensis
May-apple
Podophyllum peltatum
Bloodroot
Sanguinaria canadensis
Wood-leek
Allium tricoccum

Wood lily
Lilium philadelphicum

Upland Canada lily
Lilium canadense

Three-leaf crinkle-root
Dentaria laciniata

Solomon-plume
Smilacina racemosa

Yellow beadlily
Clintonia borealis

Northern pitcherplant
Sarracenia purpurea

Great trillium
Trillium grandiflorum

Painted trillium
Trillium undulatum

Wood-sorrel
Oxalis montana

Wood geranium
Geranium maculatum

Purple candyroot
Polygala sanguinea

White spurge
Euphorbia corollata

Touch-me-not
Impatiens biflora

Jumpseed
Tovara virginiana

Frostwort
Helianthemum canadense

Primrose violet
Viola primufolia

Canada violet
Viola canadensis

Pokeweed
Phytolacca americana

Spring-beauty
Claytonia virginica

Wild strawberry
Fragaria virginiana

Wine-leaf cinquefoil
Potentilla tridentata

Silver-and-gold
Potentilla anserina

Field cinquefoil
Potentilla canadensis

Robins-plantain
Erigeron pulchellus

Summer-aster
Seriocarpus asteroides

Swamp sneeze-weed
Helenium autumnale

American burnet
Sanguisorba canadensis

Partridge-pea
Cassia chamaecrista

Round-head bush-clover
Lespedeza capitata

Beach-pea
Lathyrus maritimus

Golden-alexander
Zizia aurea

American poison-hemlock
Cicuta maculata

Bunchberry
Cornus canadensis

Trailing-arbutus
Epigaea repens

Wintergreen
Gaultheria procumbens

Maystar
Trientalis americana

Narrow-leaf gentian
Gentiana linearis

Northern floating-heart
Nymphoides lacunosa

Butterflyweed
Asclepias tuberosa

Horse-balm
Collinsonia canadensis

Blue-eyed Mary
Collinsia verna

Eastern penstemon
Penstemon hirsutus

Partridge-berry
Mitchella repens

Star bellflower
Campanula americana

Cardinal lobelia
Lobelia cardinalis

Lime lobelia
Lobelia kalmii

Bluets
Houstonia caerulea

Joe-pye-weed
Eupatorium purpureum

Boneset
Eupatorium perfoliatum

White snake-root
Eupatorium urticaefolium

Plume goldenrod
Solidago juncea

BOGLAND WILD FLOWERS

Bog-clubmoss
Lycopodium inundatum

Hare's-tail
Eriophorum spissum

Few-flowered Sedge
Carex pauciflora

Bog-lily
Smilacina trifolia

Paper-white orchid
Habenaria blephariglottis

Swamp-pink
Pogonia ophioglossoides

Grass-pink
Calopogen pulchellus

Bog-pink
Arethusa bulbosa

Pitcher-plant
Sarracenia purpurea

Bake-apple
Rubus Chamaemorus

Bog-lambkill
Kalmia polifolia

Spice-cranberry
Vaccinium Oxycoccos

Leafless Bladderwort
Utricularia cornuta

SHRUBS

Bayberry
Myrica carolinensis

Sweet gale
Myrica gale

Sweet fern
Myrica aspenifolia

American red raspberry
Rubus idaeus

Swamp blackberry (Dewberry)
Rubus hispidus

Chokecherry
Prunus virginiana

Staghorn sumac
Rhus typhina

Common winterberry
Ilex verticillata

Serviceberry (Shadbush)
Amelanchier arborea

Inkberry
Ilex glabra

Mountain-holly
Nemopanthus mucronata

Leatherwood
Dirca palustris

Soapberry
Sherperdia canadensis

Rhododendron
Rhododendron canadense

Bearberry
Arctostaphlos ura-ursi

Scotch heather
Calluna vulgaris

Black huckleberry
Gaylussacia baccata

Sweet blueberry
Vaccinium pennsylvanicum

Canada blueberry
Vaccinium myrtilloides

Mountain cranberry (Cowberry)
Vaccinium vitis-idaea

American cranberry
Vaccinium macrocarpon

Partridge-berry
Mitchella repens

Buttonbush
Cephalanthus occidentalis

Bush honeysuckle
Diervilla lonicera

Withe-rod (Wild Raisin)
Viburnum cassinoides

Arrow-wood
Viburnum dentatum

Common elder
Sambucus canadensis

Red-berried elder
Sambucus pubens

TREES

CONIFEROUS TREES

Eastern hemlock
Tsuga canadensis

Balsam fir
Abies balsamea

White spruce
Picea glauca

Black spruce
Picea mariana

Red spruce
Picea rubens

Tamarack
Larix laricina

Eastern white pine
Pinus strobus

Red pine
Pinus resinosa

Jack pine
Pinus banksiana

Eastern white cedar
Thuja occidentalis

DECIDUOUS TREES

Black willow
Salix nigra

Peachleaf willow
Salix amygdaloides

Trembling aspen
Populus tremuloides

Balsam poplar
Populus balsamifera

Largetooth aspen
Populus grandidentata

Butternut
Juglans cinerea

Ironwood
Ostrya virginiana

Yellow birch
Betula lutea

White birch
Betula papyrifera

Wire birch
Betula populifolia

Beech
Fagus grandifolia

Bur oak
Quercus macrocarpa

Red oak
Quercus rubra

White elm
Ulmus americana

Speckled alder
Alnus rougosa

Witch-hazel
Hamamelis virginiana

Showy mountain-ash
Sorbus decora

Canada plum
Prunus nigra

Pin cherry
Prunus pensylvanica

Black cherry
Prunus serotina

Choke cherry
Prunus virginiana

Roundleaf hawthorn
Crataegus chrysocarpa

Staghorn sumac
Rhus typhina

Mountain maple
Acer spicatum

Striped maple
Acer pensylvanicum

Sugar maple
Acer saccharum

Silver maple
Acer saccharinum

Red maple
Acer rubrum

Basswood
Tilia americana

Alternate-leaf dogwood
Cornus alternifolia

White ash
Fraxinus americana

Red ash
Fraxinus pennsylvanica

Black ash
Fraxinus nigra

SEAWEED

**ALGAE WITH NEW
ENGLAND AFFILIATIONS**

Codiolum gregarium
Codiolum pussillum
Chaetomorpha atrovirens
Chaetomorpha aerea
Cladophora rupestris
Hormiscia penicilliformis
Hormiscia collabens
Hormiscia wormskjoldii
Spongomorpha arcta
Spongomorpha lanosa
Ectocarpus fasciculatus
Ralfsia clavata
Ralfsia verrucosa
Chordaria flagelliformis
Elachistea fucicola
Punctaria plantaginea
Chorda filum
Dictyosiphon foeniculaceus
Laminaria digitata
Ascophyllum nodosum
Fucus evanescens
Rhodochorton rothii
Polyides rotundus
Phyllophora brodaei

ALGAE WITH ARCTIC AFFILIATIONS

Monostroma fuscum
Monostroma pulchrum
Ectocarpus tomentosoides
Ectocarpus tomentosus
Ralfsia fungiformis
Ralfsia verrucosa
Ralfsia clavata
Chaetopteris plumosa
Holopteris scoparia
Sphacelaria radicans
Sphacelaria cirrhosa
Agarum eribrosum
Fucus edentatus
Fucus spiralis
Fucus vesiculosus
Fucus evanescens
Fucus serratus
Fucus filiformis
Fucus miclonensis

Alaria esculenta

Alaria musaefolia
Alaria membranacea
Laminaria longicruris
Laminaria stenophylla
Laminaria saccharina
Phyllaria dermatodea
Porphyra miniata
Porphyra umbilicalis
Euthora cristata
Phodophyllis dichotoma
Gigartina stellata
Halosaccion ramentaceum
Antithamnion boreale
Antithamnion floccosum
Antithamnion americanum
Plumaria pectinata
Plumaria plumosa
Plumaria sericea
Membranoptera denticulata
Odenthalia dentata

**ARCTIC ALGAE REACHING
NEWFOUNDLAND**

Omphalophyllum ulvaceum
Laminaria groenlandica
Laminaria solidungula
Trunella pennyi
Dilsea integ
Pantoneura baerii
Polysiphonia arctica

ANIMALS

SEA AND INTERTIDAL ANIMALS

The crumb of bread sponge
Halichondria panicea

Eyed finger sponge
Chalina oculata

The pink jellyfish
Gyanea capillata

The white sea jelly
Aurelia aurita

The sea-cauliflower
Duva multiflora

The bush coral
Acanella normani

Northern comb jelly
Beroe cucumis

Sea mouse
Aphrodite aculeata

Common serpula
Serpula vermicularis

Northern coil worm
Spirorbis borealis

Brown anemone
Metridium dianthus

MOLLUSCS

Common scallop
Pecten irradians

Iceland scallop
Chlamys islandicus

Giant scallop
Placopecten magellanicus

Common edible mussel
Mytilus edulis

Ribbed mussel
Modiolus demissus

Thorny jungle shell
Anomia aculeata

Smooth jungle shell
Anomia simplex

American oyster
Ostrea virginica

Lantern shell
Periploma leanum

Chestnut astarte
Astarte castanea

Wavy astarte
Astarte undata

Northern astarte
Astarte borealis

Northern heart shell
Venericardia borealis

Iceland cockle
Cardium ciliatum

Morton's cockle
Cardium (Laevicardium) mortoni

Wavy carpet shell
Liocyma (Tapes) fluctuosa

Delicate tellin
Tellina tenera

Little macoma
Macoma balthica

Scaly pod shell
Siliqua squama

Rough piddock
Zirjaea crispata

Ship worm
Teredo navalis

Common tooth shell
Dentalium entale

Ocean quahog
Artica islandica

Northern quahog (hard shell clam, little-neck, cherry-stone)
Venus (Mercenaria) mercenaria

Morrhua venus (false venus)
Pitar morrhuana

Amethyst gem clam
Gemma gemma

Arctic wedge clam
Mesodesma arctatum

Arctic surf clam (bar clam or hen clam)
Spisula solidissimia

Stimpson's surf clam
Spisula polynyma

Dwarf surf clam
Mulinia lateralis

Atlantic flat lepton
Mysella planulata

Dwarf turton clam
Turtonia minuta

Common razor clam
(jacknife clam)
Ensis directus

Ribbed pod shell
Siliqua costata

False angel wing
Petricola pholadiformis

Arctic saxicave
Hiatella Arctica

Northern propeller clam (banks clam)
Cyrtodaria siliqua

Great (or rough) piddock
Zirphaea crispata

Fallen angel wing
Barnea truncata

Common soft-shell clam (Long-neck clam)
Mya arenaria

Boreal awning clam
Solemya borealis

Tortoise-shell limpet
Acmaea testudinalis

Little chink
Puncturella princeps

Ladder shell
Epitonium (scalaria) groenlandicum

Little moon shell
Natica clausa

Moon shell
Polinices heros

Cup-and-saucer limpet
Crucibulum striatum

Boat shell
Crepidula fornicata

Flat slipper
Crepidula plana

Orb shell
Skenea planorbis

Common periwinkle
Littorina litorea

Rough periwinkle
Littorina rudis

Northern hairy keel
Trichotropis borealis

Oyster drill
Urosalpinx cinerea

Mud snail
Nassa (Alectrion) obsoleta

Dog whelk
Nassa (Alectrion) bivittata

Ten-ridged neptune
Neptunea (Chrysodomus) decemcostata

Stimpson's distaff shell
Colus (Sipho) stimpsoni

Plumed sea slug
Aeolis (Aeolidia) papillosa

Short-finned squid
Illex illecebrosus

Squid
Rossia hyatti

Giant squid
Architeuthis princeps

CRUSTACEANS

Barnacles

Common goose barnacle
Lepas anatifera

Common rock barnacle
Balanus balanoides

Notched acorn barnacle
Balanus crenatus

Little ivory barnacle
Balanus improvisus

Northern ridged barnacle
Balanus balanus

Turban barnacle
Balanus hamera

Shrimps, Crayfish, Lobsters, Crabs

American lobster
Homarus americanus

Common rock crab
Cancer irroratus

Green crab
Carcinides maenas

Jonah crab
Cancer borealis

ARACHNIDS

Horseshoe crab
Limulus polyphemus

ECHINODERMS

Purple starfish
Asterial vulgaris

Polar (or six-rayed) starfish
Peltasterias polaris

Blood sea-star
Henricia sanguinolenta

Green sea urchin
Strongylocentrotus drobachiensis

Common sand dollar
Echinarachnius parma

Common sun-star
Crossaster papposus

Slender-armed sea-star
Asterias tenera

Greenland starfish
Leptasterias groenlandica

Polar starfish
Leptasterias polaris

Müller's starfish
Lepasterias mülleri

Daisy brittle-star
Ophiopholis aculeata

Long-armed snake-star
Amphipholis squamata

MOSS ANIMALS

Broad-leaved hornwrack
Flustra foliacea

LAMP SHELLS

Northern lamp shell
Terebratulina septentrionalis

Parrot-beak lamp shell
Hemithyris psittacea

INSECTS

PRINCIPAL MARITIME
FOREST INSECTS

Spruce budworm
Choristoneura fumiferana

Balsam woolly aphid
Adelges piceae

Balsam gall midge
Dasineura balsamicola

Larch sawfly
Pristiphora erichsonii

Winter moth
Operophtera brumata

Bruce spanworm
Operophtera bruceata

Birch leaf miner
Fenusa pusilla

Fall cankerworm
Alsophila pometaria

Birch casebearer
Coleophora fuscedinella

Larch casebearer
Colephora laricella

European pine shoot moth
Rhyacionia buoliana

Spring cankerworm
Paleacrita vernata

Forest tent caterpillar
Malacosoma disstria

Satin moth
Stilpnotia salicis

Balsam-fir sawfly
Neodiprion abietis

European spruce sawfly
Diprion hercyniae

A maple leaf roller
Cenopis pettitana

Birch skeletonizer
Bucculatrix canadensisella

Red-headed jack-pine sawfly
Neodiprion virginianus

Ugly-nest caterpillar
Archips cerasivoranus

Fall webworm
Hyphantria cunea

ROACHES, GRASSHOPPERS,
CRICKETS, ALLIES

Common walkingstick
Diapheromera femorata

Cave cricket
Ceuthophilus gracilipes

Common field cricket
Acheta assimils

Northern mole cricket
Gryllotalpa hexadactyla

EARWIGS

European earwig
Forficula auricularia

STONEFLIES

Stonefly
Neophasganophora capitata

BUGS, APHIDS,
SCALES and ALLIES

Ground bug
Pangaeus bilineatus

Squash bug
Anasa tristis

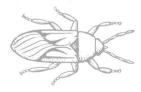

Chinch bug
Blissus leucopterus

Damsel bug
Nabis ferus

Water strider
Gerris marginatus

Backswimmer
Notonecta undulata

Water boatman
Arctocorixa interrupta

LEAFHOPPERS, APHIDS,
SCALES and ALLIES

Planthopper
Ormensis septentrionalis

Periodical cicada
Magicicada septendecim

Buffalo Treehopper
Ceresa bubalus

Spittlebug
Aphrophora quadrinotata

Red-banded leafhopper
Graphocephala coccinea

Green peach aphid
Myzus persicae

DAMSELFLIES and DRAGONFLIES

Common bluet
Enallagma ebrium

Big green darner
Anax junius

Ten spot
Libellula pulchella

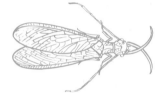

NERVE-WINGED INSECTS

Dobsonfly
Corydalus cornutus

Brown lacewing
Boriomyia fidelis

Antlion
Myrmeleon immaculatus

CADDISFLIES

Large caddisfly
Ptilostomis semifasciata

MOTHS and BUTTERFLIES

Luna moth
Tropaea luna

Zebra swallowtail
Iphiclides marcellus

Monarch butterfly
Danaus plexippus

Grayling
Minois alope

Red admiral
Vanessa atalanta

MARINE FISH

Sea lamprey
Petromyzon marinus

Porbeagle
Lamna nasus

Spiny dogfish
Squalus acanthias

Barndoor skate
Raja laevis

Winter skate
Raja ocellata

Thorny skate
Raja radiata

Smooth skate
Raja senta

Spinytail skate
Raja spinicauda

Shortnose sturgeon
Acipenser brevirostrum

Atlantic sturgeon
Acipenser oxyrhynchus

Alewife
Alosa pseudoharengus

American shad
Alosa sapidissima
Atlantic herring
Clupea harengus
Atlantic salmon
Salmo salar
Brown trout
Salmo trutta
Arctic char
Salvelinus alpinus
Capelin
Mallotus villosus
American smelt
Osmerus mordax
Atlantic argentine
Argentina silus
American eel
Anguilla rostrata
Atlantic saury
Scomberesox saurus
Fourspine stickleback
Apeltes quadracus
Atlantic cod
Gadus morhua
Haddock
Melanogrammus aeglefinus
Silver hake
Merluccius bilinearis

Atlantic tomcod
Microgadus tomcod

Pollock
Pollachius virens
White hake
Urophycis tenuis
Rock grenadier
Coryphaenoides rupestris
Roughhead grenadier
Macrourus berglax
Striped bass
Roccus saxatilis
Lumpfish
Cyclopterus lumpus

Northern sand launce
Ammodytes dubius
Atlantic mackerel
Scomber scombrus
Bluefin tuna
Thunnus thynnus
Swordfish
Xiphias gladius
Northern wolffish
Anarhichas denticulatus
Atlantic wolffish
Anarhichas lupus
Spotted wolffish
Anarichas minor
Ocean pout
Macrozoarces americanus
Redfish (Ocean Perch)
Sebastes marinus
Rosefish (Ocean Perch)
Sebastes mentella
Witch flounder
Glyptocephalus cynoglossus
American plaice
Hippoglossoides platessoides
Atlantic halibut
Hippoglossus hippoglossus
Yellowtail flounder
Limanda ferruginea
Winter flounder
Pseudopleuronectes americanus
Greenland halibut
Reinhardtius hippoglossoides
Monkfish
Lophius americanus

FRESHWATER FISH

Atlantic salmon (Ouananiche)
Salmo salar
Brook trout
Salvelinus fontinalis
Lake trout
Salvelinus namaycush
Lake whitefish
Coregonus clupeaformis
Round whitefish
Prosopium cylindraceum
Chain pickerel
Esox niger
Northern pike
Esox lucius
Longnose sucker
Catostomus catostomus

White sucker
Catostomus commersoni

Pearl dace
Semotilus margarita
Fallfish
Semotilus corporalis
Creek chub
Semotilus atromaculatis
Redbelly dace
Chrosomus eos
Golden shiner
Notemigonuscrysoleucas
Common shiner
Notropis cornutus
Blacknose shiner
Notropis heterolepis
Brook stickleback
Eucalia inconstans
Threespine stickleback
Gasterosteus aculeatus
White perch
Roccus americanus
Pumpkinseed
Lepomis gibbosus
Yellowbelly sunfish
Lepomis auritus
Yellow perch
Perca flavescens
Mottled sculpin
Cottus bairdi
Slimy sculpin
Cottus cognatus

REPTILES AND AMPHIBIANS

Snapping turtle
Chelydra serpentina
Wood turtle
Clemmys insculpta
Eastern painted turtle
Chrysemys picta
Atlantic loggerhead
Caretta caretta

Atlantic ridley
Lepidochelys kempi
Atlantic leatherback
Dermochelys coriacea
Eastern garter snake
Thamnophis sirtalis
Eastern ribbon snake
Thamnophis sauritus
Northern black racer
Coluber constrictor
Spotted salamander
Ambystoma maculatum
Red-spotted newt
Diemictylus viridescens viridescens
Northern dusky salamander
Desmognathus fuscus
Red-backed salamander
Plethodon cinereus
American toad
Bufo americanus
Spring peeper
Hyla crucifer
Bullfrog
Rana catesbeiana
Mink frog
Rana septentrionalis
Green frog
Rana clamitans
Leopard frog
Rana pipiens
Pickerel frog
Rana palustris
Wood frog
Rana sylvatica

BIRDS

BIRDS OF THE SEA,
FRESH WATER AND SHORE

Common loon
Gavia immer
Red-throated loon
Gavia stellata
Horned grebe
Podiceps auritus
Fulmar
Fulmarus glacialis
Greater shearwater
Puffinus gravis
Sooty shearwater
Puffinus griseus
Leach's petrel
Oceanodroma leucorhoa

Wilson's petrel
Oceanites oceanicus

Gannet
Morus bassanus

Great cormorant
Phalacrocorax carbo

Double-crested cormorant
Phalacrocorax auritus

Great blue heron
Ardea herodias

Least bittern
Ixobrychus exilis

American bittern
Botaurus lentiginosus

Canada goose
Branta canadensis

Brant
Branta bernicla

Mallard
Anas platyrhynchos

Black duck
Anas rubripes

Pintail
Anas acuta

Green-winged teal
Anas carolinensis

Blue-winged teal
Anas discors

Wood duck
Aix sponsa

Ring-necked duck
Aythya collaris

Greater scaup
Aythya marila

Lesser scaup
Aythya affinis

Common goldeneye
Bucephala clangula

Barrow's goldeneye
Bucephala islandica

Bufflehead
Bucephala albeola

Oldsquaw
Clangula hyemalis

Harlequin duck
Histrionicus histrionicus

Common eider
Somateria mollissima

King eider
Somateria spectabilis

White-winged scoter
Melanitta deglandi

Surf scoter
Melanitta perapicillata

Common scoter
Oidemia nigra

Common merganser
Mergus merganser

Red-breasted merganser
Mergus serrator

Virginia rail
Rallus limicola

Sora
Porzana carolina

Semipalmated plover
Charadrius semipalmatus

Piping plover
Charadrius melodus

Black-bellied plover
Squatarola squatarola

Whimbrel
Numenius phaeopus

Spotted sandpiper
Actitis macularia

Solitary sandpiper
Tringa solitaria

Greater yellowlegs
Totanus melanoleucus

Lesser yellowlegs
Totanus flavipes

Knot
Calidris canutus

Willet
Catoptrophorus semipalmatus

Purple Sandpiper
Erolia maritima

Pectoral sandpiper
Erolia melanotos

White-rumped sandpiper
Erolia fuscicollis

Least sandpiper
Erolia minutilla

Dunlin
Erolia alpina

Short-billed dowitcher
Limnodromus griseus

Semipalmated sandpiper
Ereunetes pusillus

Sanderling
Crocethia alba

Red phalarope
Phalaropus fulicarius

Northern phalarope
Lobipes lobatus

Pomarine jaeger
Stercorarius pomarinus

Parasitic jaeger
Stercorarius parasiticus

Glaucous gull
Larus hyperboreus

Iceland gull
Larus glaucoides

Great black-backed gull
Larus marinus

Herring gull
Larus argentatus

Ring-billed gull
Larus delawarensis

Black-headed gull
Larus ridibundus

Laughing gull
Larus atricilla

Bonaparte's gull
Larus philadelphia

Black-legged kittiwake
Rissa tridactyla

Common tern
Sterna hirundo

Arctic tern
Sterna paradisaea

Razorbill
Alca torda

Common murre
Uria aalge

Thick-billed murre
Urialomvia

Dovekie
Plautus alle

Black guillemot
Cepphus grylle

Common puffin
Fratercula arctica

Belted kingfisher
Megaceryle alcyon

Northern waterthrush
Selurus noveboracensis

BIRDS OF PREY

Turkey vulture
Cathartes aura

Goshawk
Accipiter striatus

Sharp-shinned hawk
Accipiter striatus

Red-tailed hawk
Buteo jamaicensis

Broad-winged hawk
Buteo platypterus

Rough-legged hawk
Buteo lagopus

Bald eagle
Haliaeetus leucocephalus

Marsh hawk
Circus cyaneus

Osprey
Pandion haliaetus

Peregrine falcon
Falco peregrinus

Sparrow hawk
Falco sparverius

Great horned owl
Bubo virginianus

Snowy owl
Nyctea scandiaca

Barred owl
Strix varia

Long-eared owl
Asio otus

Saw-whet owl
Aegolius acadicus

LAND BIRDS

Spruce grouse
Canachites canadensis

Ruffed grouse
Bonasa umbellus

Ring-necked pheasant
Phasianus colchicus

Gray partridge
Perdix perdix

American woodcock
Philohela minor

Common snipe
Capella gallinago

Rock dove (Domestic Pigeon)
Columba livia

Black-billed cuckoo
Coccyzus erythropthalmus

Whip-poor-will
Caprimulgus vociferus

Common nighthawk
Chordeiles minor

Chimney swift
Chaetura pelagica

Ruby-throated hummingbird
Archilochus colubris

Yellow-shafted flicker
Colaptes auratus

Pileated woodpecker
Dryocopus pileatus

Yellow-bellied sapsucker
Sphyrapicus varius

Hairy woodpecker
Dendrocopos villosus

Downy woodpecker
Dendrocopos pubescens

Eastern kingbird
Tyrannus tyrannus

Yellow-bellied flycatcher
Empidonax flaviventris

Traill's flycatcher
Empidonax traillii

Least flycatcher
Empidonax minimus

Eastern wood pewee
Contopus virens

Olive-sided flycatcher
Nuttallornis borealis

Horned lark
Eremophila alpestris

Tree swallow
Iridoprocne bicolor

Bank swallow
Riparia riparia

Barn swallow
Hirundo rustica

Cliff swallow (Eave Swallow)
Petrochelidon pyrrhonota

Purple martin
Progne subis

Gray jay
Perisoreus canadensis

Blue jay
Cyanocitta cristata

Common raven
Corvus corax

Common crow
Corvus brachyrhynchos

Black-capped chickadee
Parus atricapillus

Boreal chickadee (Acadian Chickadee)
Parus hudsonicus

White-breasted nuthatch
Sitta carolinensis

Red-breasted nuthatch
Sitta canadensis

Brown creeper
Certhia familiaris

Long-billed marsh wren
Telmatodytes palustris

Catbird
Dumetella carolinensis

Robin
Turdus migratorius

Hermit thrush
Hylocichla guttata

Swainson's thrush
(Olive-backed Thrush)
Hylocichla ustulata

Gray-cheeked thrush
Hylocichla minima

Veery
Hylocichla fuscescens

Eastern bluebird
Sialia sialis

Golden-crowned kinglet
Regulus satrapa

Ruby-crowned kinglet
Regulus calendula

Water pipit
Anthus spinoletta

Cedar waxwing
Bombycilla cedrorum

Northern shrike
Lanius excubitor

Starling
Sturnus vulgaris

Solitary vireo
Vireo solitarius

Red-eyed vireo
Vireo olivaceus

Black and white warbler
Mniotilla varia

Tennessee warbler
Vermivora peregrina

Nashville warbler
Vermivora ruficapilla

Parula warbler
Parula americana

Yellow warbler
Dendroica petechia

Magnolia warbler
Dendroica magnolia

Cape May warbler
Dendroica tigrina

Black-throated blue warbler
Dendroica caerulescens

Myrtle warbler
Dendroica coronata

Black-throated green warbler
Dendroica virens

Blackburnian warbler
Dendroica fusca

Chestnut-sided warbler
Dendroica pensylvanica

Bay-breasted warbler
Dendroica castanea

Blackpoll warbler
Dendroica striata

Palm warbler
(Yellow Palm Warbler)
Dendroica palmarum

Ovenbird
Seiurus aurocapillus

Mourning warbler
Oporornis philadelphia

Yellowthroat
Geothlypis trichas

Canada warbler
Wilsonia canadensis

American redstart
Setophaga ruticilla

House sparrow
(English sparrow)
Passer domesticus

Bobolink
Dolichonyx oryzivorus

Eastern meadowlark
Sturnella magna

Redwinged blackbird
Agelaius phoeniceus

Baltimore oriole
Icterus galbula

Rusty blackbird
Euphagus carolinus

Common grackle
(bronzed grackle)
Quiscalus quiscula

Brown-headed cowbird
(eastern cowbird)
Molothrus ater

Rose-breasted grosbeak
Pheucticus ludovicianus

Evening grosbeak
Hesperiphona vespertina

Pine siskin
Spinus pinus

151

Purple finch
Carpodacus purpureus
Pine grosbeak
Pinicola enucleator
Common redpoll
Acanthis flammea
American goldfinch
Spinus tristis
Red crossbill
Loxia curvirostra
White-winged crossbill
Loxia leucoptera
Ipswich sparrow
Passerculus princeps
Savannah sparrow
Passerculus sandwichensis
Sharp-tailed sparrow
Ammospiza caudacuta
Vesper sparrow
Pooecetes gramineus
Slate-colored junco
Junco hyemalis
Tree sparrow
Spizella arborea
Chipping sparrow
Spizella passerina
White-throated sparrow
Zonotrichia albicollis
Fox sparrow
Passerella iliaca
Lincoln's sparrow
Melospiza lincolnii
Swamp sparrow
Melospiza georgiana
Song sparrow
Melospiza melodia
Lapland longspur
Calcarius lapponicus
Snow bunting
Plectrophenax nivalis

LAND MAMMALS

MOLES AND SHREWS
Common or Masked shrew
Sorex cinereus
Smoky shrew
Sorex fumeus
Gaspé shrew
Sorex gaspensis
Northern water shrew
Sorex palustris

Pigmy shrew
Microsorex hoyi
Big short-tailed shrew
   (Mole-shrew)
Blarina brevicauda
Hairy-tailed mole
   (Brewer's Mole)
Parascalops breweri
Star-nosed mole
Condylura cristata

BATS
Little brown bat
Myotis lucifugus
Silver-haired bat
Lasionycteris noctivagans
Pipistrelles
Pipistrellus subflavus
Big brown bat
Eptesicus fuscus
Red bat
Lasiurus borealis
Hoary bat
Lasiurus cinereus

PIKAS, HARES AND RABBITS
Varying hare
   (Snowshoe Hare or Rabbit)
Lepus americanus
Arctic hare
Lepus arcticus

MARMOTS, SQUIRRELS AND CHIPMUNKS
Gray squirrel
Sciurus carolinensis
Red squirrel (Chickarees)
Tamiasciurus hudsonicus
Eastern chipmunk
Tamias striatus
Flying squirrel
Glaucomys sabrinus
Woodchuck (Chuck,
Ground Hog)
Marmota monax

BEAVER
Beaver
Castor canadensis

MICE, RATS, VOLES AND LEMMINGS
Deer mouse
Peromyscus maniculatus
Lemming mice (Bog lemmings)
Synaptomys cooperi
Red-backed mouse
Clethrionomys gapperi
Meadow vole
Microtus pennsylvanicus
Yellow-nosed or rock vole
Microtus chrotorrhinus
Muskrat (Musquash)
Ondatra zibethious

MEADOW JUMPING MICE
Northern jumping mouse
Zapus hudsonius
Woodland jumping mouse
Napaeozapus insignis

PORCUPINES
Porcupine
Erethizon dorsatum

FOXES, WOLVES AND DOGS
Gray or timber wolf
Canis lupus
Red fox (Colored fox)
Vulpes fulva

WEASELS, SKUNKS AND ALLIES
Short-tailed weasel (Ermine)
Mustela erminea
Long-tailed weasel
Mustela frenata
Mink
Mustela vison
Marten (Sable)
Martes americana
Fisher (Blackcat)
Martes pennanti
River otter
Lutra canade

CATS
Lynx (Canada lynx)
Lynx canadensis
Bobcat (Wildcat, Bay Lynx)
Lynx rufus

DEER
Moose
Alces alces
Caribou
Rangifer tarandus

MARINE MAMMALS

SEALS AND SEA LIONS
Harbor seal (Common seal)
Phoca vitulina
Ringed seal (Jar seal)
Pusa hispida
Harp seal (Saddleback seal)
Phoca groenlandica
Gray seal (Horsehead)
Halichoerus grypus
Hooded seal (Bladdernose)
Cystophora cristata

WHALES, DOLPHINS AND PORPOISES
Bottlenose whale
Hyperoodon ampullatus
Sperm whale
Physeter catodon
White whale
Delphinapterus leucas
Dolphin (Common dolphin)
Delphinus delphis
White-beaked dolphin
   (Squidhound)
Lagenorhynchus albirostris
Killer whale
Orcinus grampus
Pilot whale
   (Pothead, Roundhead)
Globicephala melaena
Harbour porpoise
Phocoena phocoena
Fin whale
Balaenoptera physalus
Sei whale
Balaenoptera borealis
Blue whale
Sibbaldus musculus
Humpback whale
Megaptera novaeangliae
Right whale
Eubalaena glacialis

Large scale maps and other information on the Atlantic Coast region can be obtained at moderate cost from: Department of Mines, Agriculture and Resources, St. John's, Newfoundland; Department of Lands and Forests, Halifax, Nova Scotia; Department of Tourist Development, Charlottetown, Prince Edward Island; Canada Department of Energy, Mines and Resources, 601 Booth Street, Ottawa, Ontario. A selection of film strips and slides is available from: National Film Board, P.O. Box 6100, Montreal 3, Quebec.

BIBLIOGRAPHY

REGIONAL

CLARK, ANDREW HILL.
Three Centuries and the Island.
University of Toronto Press, 1959.

HAMELIN, LOUIS.
Sables et Mer aux Iles-de-la-Madeleine.
Québec: Beaulieu, 1959.

HOWLEY, JAMES P.
Geological Survey of Newfoundland.
London: E. Stanford, 1881.

JANES, L. W. (ed.)
The Treasury of Newfoundland Stories.
St. John's: Maple Leaf Mills Ltd.

JUKES, J. B.
Excursions in and about Newfoundland during the years of 1839 and 1840.
London: J. Murray, 1842.

LAUZIER, L. M. and HULL, J. H.
Sea Temperatures along the Canadian Atlantic Coast 1958-60.
Ottawa: Fisheries Research Board, Atlantic Progress Report No. 73, 1960.

LOUNSBURY, R. G.
The British Fishery at Newfoundland, 1634-1763.
Yale University Press, 1934.

MACBEATH, GEORGE B.
The Story of the Restigouche.
St. John: New Brunswick Museum, Historical Studies No. 8, 1954.

MCCURDY, J. A. D.
Nova Scotia and the Men who Lived on her Soil.
New York: Newcomen Society, 1953.

MILLAIS, J. G.
Newfoundland and its Untrodden Ways.
London: Longmann Green, 1907.

MORLEY, W. F.
The Atlantic Provinces: Newfoundland, Nova Scotia, New Brunswick, Prince Edward Island.
Toronto: University of Toronto Press, 1967.

OUTHWAITE, LEONARD.
The Atlantic.
New York: Coward-McCann, 1957.

SHARPLES, ALICE.
Ports of Pine: Labrador-Newfoundland-Gaspé.
Montreal: Clarke Steamship Co., 1939.

STEWART, JOHN.
An Account of Prince Edward Island in the Gulf of St. Lawrence, North America.
New York: Johnson Reprint Corp., 1967.

WEAVER, J. E. and CLEMENTS, F. E.
Plant Ecology.
New York: McGraw-Hill, 1938.

WHITBOURNE, SIR RICHARD.
Westward Hoe for Avalon in the New-found-land. (As described by Captain Richard Whitbourne of Exmouth, Devon, 1622).
London: S. Low, Son, and Marston, 1870.

PERIODICALS

Acadiensis (St. John, N.B.)
Volumes 1-8, 1901-1908.

HARE, F. K.
"Climate and Zonal Divisions of the Boreal Forest Formation in Eastern Canada."
Geographical Review, 40 (4), 1950.

PUTNAM, D. F.
"The Climate of the Maritime Provinces."
Canadian Geographical Journal, 21 (3), 1940.

ANIMALS

ALLEN, K. R. and SAUNDERS, R. L.
A Preliminary Study of the Influence of the Greenland Salmon Fishery on the Salmon Stocks and Fishery of the Miramichi River, New Brunswick, Canada.
Ottawa: Fisheries Research Board of Canada, Biological Station, St. Andrews.

AMOS, WILLIAM H.
The Life of the Seashore.
Toronto: McGraw-Hill, 1966.

ANDERSON, R. M.
Catalogue of Canadian Recent Mammals.
National Museum of Canada, Bulletin 102, 1946.

ANON.
Stock-taking of Molluscan Shellfish Resources and Prospects for Improvement.
Atlantic Coast Stations, Progress Reports Issue No. 71, 1958.

AUDUBON, J. J.
The Birds of America.
New York: 1840.

BLEAKNEY, J. S.
A Zoogeographical Study of the Amphibians and Reptiles of Eastern Canada.
National Museum of Canada, Bull. 155, 1958.

BOURNE, N.
Scallops and the Offshore Fishery of the Maritimes.
Fisheries Research Board, Bull. 145, 1964.

BOUSFIELD, E. L.
Canadian Atlantic Seashells.
National Museum of Canada, 1960.

BREDER, CHARLES M., JR.
Marine Fishes of the Atlantic Coast.
New York: Putnam, 1948.

BURT, W. H.
A Field Guide to the Mammals.
Boston: Houghton-Mifflin, 1964.

CAHALANE, VICTOR H.
Mammals of North America.
New York: Macmillan, 1954.

CAMERON, AUSTIN W.
*Mammals of the Islands in
the Gulf of St. Lawrence.*
National Museum of Canada, Bull. 154, 1958.

CONANT, R.
*A Field Guide to the Reptiles and
Amphibians of Eastern North America.*
Boston: Houghton-Mifflin, 1958.

COOK, FRANCIS R.
*An Analysis of the Herpetofauna
of Prince Edward Island.*
National Museum of Canada, Bull. 212, 1967.

DOW, ROBERT L. and WALLACE, DANA E.
The Maine Clams.
Augusta, Maine: Bulletin of the Department
of Sea and Shore Fisheries.

FISHER, JAMES and LOCKLEY, R. M.
Sea-Birds.
Boston: Houghton-Mifflin, 1954.

GRIEVE, SYMINGTON.
The Great Auk, or Garefowl.
London: 1885.

HYMAN, L. H.
*The Invertebrates: Protozoa
through Ctenophora.*
New York: McGraw-Hill, 1940.

INNIS, HAROLD.
*The Cod Fisheries, the History
of an International Economy.*
New Haven, Yale Univ. Press, 1940.

LAMBE, L. M.
Sponges from the Atlantic Coast of Canada.
Transactions Royal Society of
Canada, 2 (2), 1896.

LOCKLEY, R. M.
Puffins.
New York: Doubleday, 1962.

MARTIN, J. L.
*The Amphibians and Reptiles
of Nova Scotia.*
Halifax: Nova Scotia Museum.

MAYER, A. G.
*Ctenophores of the Atlantic
Coast of North America.*
Washington: Carnegie Institute,
Pub. 162, (3 vols), 1912.

MCKENZIE, R. A.
*Smelt, Life History and Fishery in
the Miramichi River, New Brunswick.*
Fisheries Research Board, Bull. 144, 1964.

MORRIS, P. A.
*A Field Guide to the Shells
of our Atlantic Coast.*
New York: 1947.

PETERS, HAROLD S., and BURLEIGH, T. D.
Birds of Newfoundland.
St. John's: Dept. of Natural Resources, 1951.

PETERSON, R. L.
Mammals of Eastern Canada.
Toronto: Oxford Univ. Press, 1966.

RUTHERFORD, W. J. B., WILDER, D. C.,
and FRICK, H. C.
*An Economic Appraisal of the
Canadian Lobster Fishery.*
Fisheries Research Board, Bull. 16, 1967.

SCHMIDT, K. P. and DAVIS, D. D.
*Field Book of Snakes of
North America and Canada.*
New York: Putnam, 1941.

SCHMIDT, K. P.
*Checklist of North American
Amphibians and Reptiles.* 6th edition.
Chicago: Univ. of Chicago Press, 1950.

SCOTT, FREDERICK.
The Seals of Nova Scotian Waters.
Halifax: Nova Scotia Museum, 1968.

SCOTT, W. B. and CROSSMAN, E. J.
Fishes of Newfoundland.
Toronto: Royal Ontario Museum, 1964.

SCOTT, W. B., and CARRICK, W. H.
Freshwater Fishes of Eastern Canada.
Toronto: Univ. of Toronto Press, 1967.

SERGEANT, D. E.
*Minke Whales, Balaenoptera Acutorostrata
Lacepede, of the Western North Atlantic.*
Montreal: Fisheries Research Board, Arctic
Unit, Circular 20, 1963.

SERGEANT, D. E.
*The Biology and Hunting of Beluga
or White Whales in the Canadian Arctic.*
Montreal: Fisheries Research Board, Arctic
Unit, Circular 8, 1962.

SERGEANT, D. E.
*Whales and Dolphins of the
Canadian East Coast.*
Montreal: Fisheries Research Board, Arctic
Unit, Circular 7, 1961.

SERGEANT, D. E.
*Populations of Large Whale Species in
the Western North Atlantic with Special
Reference to the Fin Whale.*
Montreal: Fisheries Research Board, Arctic
Unit, Circular 9, 1966.

SQUIRES, W. A.
The Birds of New Brunswick.
St. John: New Brunswick Museum, 1952.

TEMPLEMAN, W. F.
Marine Resources of Newfoundland.
Ottawa: Fisheries Research Board,
Bulletin 154, 1966.

TIBBO, S. N., DAY, L. R., and DOUCET, W. F.
*The Swordfish, its Life History and
Economic Importance in Northwest Atlantic.*
Ottawa: Fisheries Research Board,
Bulletin 130, 1961.

TUCK, LESLIE M.
*The Chronology in Canada of the
Spring Migration of Snipe.*
Ottawa: Canadian Wildlife Service, Snipe
Investigations Progress Report No. 1, 1962.

TUCK, LESLIE M.
The Murres.
Ottawa: Canadian Wildlife Service, 1961.

TUFTS, ROBIE W.
The Birds of Nova Scotia.
Halifax: Nova Scotia Museum, 1961.

WILDER, D. G.
Canadian Atlantic Crab Resources.
Ottawa: Fisheries Research Board.
Circular 50, 1966.

PERIODICALS

MACPHAIL, J. S. and MEDCOF, J. C.
"Ocean Quahaug Explorations."
Trade News, Dept. of Fisheries, 1959.

MEDCOF, J. C.
"Shellfish Poisoning—Another
North American Ghost."
Canadian Medical Association Journal,
January, 1960.

PETERS, STUART S.
"Food Habits of the Newfoundland
Willow Ptarmigan."
Journal of Wildlife Management,
Volume 22, No. 4, 1958.

PLANTS

BRAUN, E. LUCY.
*The Deciduous Forests of
Eastern North America.*
Philadelphia: Blakiston, 1950.

COBB, B.
A Field Guide to the Ferns.
Boston: Houghton-Mifflin, 1963.

CUNNINGHAM, G. C.
Forest Flora of Canada.
Ottawa: Queen's Printer, Department
of Forestry and Rural Development.

DAMMAN, A. W. H.
*Some Forest Types of Central Newfoundland
and their Relation to Environmental Factors.*
Forest Research Branch Contribution 596,
Department of Forestry, Canada and Forest
Science Monograph No. 8, Society of American
Foresters Publication, 1964.

Native Trees of Canada.
Ottawa: Queen's Printer,
Bulletin No. 61, 1956.

*Annual Report of the Forest
Insect and Disease Survey.*
Ottawa: Dept. of Forestry, 1966.

DRINKWATER, M. H.
*The Tolerant Hardwood Forests
of Northern Nova Scotia.*
Dept. of Northern Affairs and National
Resources, Forest Research Note No. 57.

ERSKINE, DAVID S.
The Plants of Prince Edward Island.
Department of Agriculture, 1961.

ERSKINE, J. S.
Under the Forest.
Halifax: Nova Scotia Museum, 1959.

ERSKINE, J. S.
An Introduction to Nova Scotian Mosses.
Halifax: Nova Scotia Museum, 1956.

ERSKINE, J. S.
Bogs and their Plants.
Halifax: Nova Scotia Museum, 1957.

FERNALD, M. L.
Gray's Manual of Botany.
New York: American Book Co., 1950.

FERNALD, M. L.
Unglaciated Western Newfoundland.
Harvard Alumni Bulletin, 1930.

FERNALD, M. L.
Two Summers of Botanizing in Newfoundland.
Gray Herbarium of Harvard Univ., 1926.

FERNOW, B. E.
Forest Conditions of Nova Scotia.
Ottawa: Department of Crown Lands, 1912.

GLEASON, HENRY A.
*The New Britton and Brown Illustrated
Flora of the Northeastern United
States and Adjacent Canada.*
New York: Hafner, 1952.

LOUCKS, O. L.
*A Forest Classification for
the Maritime Provinces.*
Ottawa: Dept. of Forestry, 1959-60.

MACFARLANE, CONSTANCE I.
Irish Moss in the Maritime Provinces.
Halifax: Nova Scotia Research
Foundation, 1956.

MACFARLANE, CONSTANCE I.
*Sublittoral Surveying for Commercial
Seaweeds in Northumberland Strait.*
Halifax: Fifth International
Seaweed Symposium, 1965.

MATHEWS, F. S.
Field Book of American Trees and Shrubs.
New York: Putnam, 1915.

MERCIER, HONORÉ.
*The Forests and Waterfalls of
the Province of Quebec.*
Quebec: Dept. Lands & Forests, 1927.

PETERSON, R. T.
*A Field Guide to Wildflowers of
Northeastern and Northcentral America.*
Boston: Houghton-Mifflin, 1968.

PETRIDES, G. A.
*Field Guide to Trees and Shrubs (of
Northeastern and Central North America).*
New York: Houghton-Mifflin, 1968.

ROLAND, A. E.
The Flora of Nova Scotia.
Nova Scotia Institute of Science,
Volume XXI, 1944-45.

ROWE, J. S.
Forest Regions of Canada.
Ottawa: Department of Northern Affairs
and National Resources, Forestry Branch
Bulletin 123, 1959.

SARGENT, C. S.
Manual of the Trees of North America.
Boston: Houghton-Mifflin, 1905.

GEOLOGY

BAIRD, DAVID M.
Rocks and Scenery of Fundy National Park.
Ottawa: Geological Survey of Canada, 1964.

BAIRD, DAVID M.
*The Living Sands (Prince
Edward Island).*
Ottawa: Geological Survey of Canada, 1963.

FLINT, R. F.
Glacial and Pleistocene Geology.
New York: John Wiley, 1957.

Geology of Nova Scotia.
Halifax: Department of Mines, 1953.

GESNER, ABRAHAM.
*Report on the Geological Survey of
the Province of New Brunswick, 1838-1842.*
Saint John: H. Chubb, 1839-1843.

GILPIN, EDWIN.
The Minerals of Nova Scotia.
Ottawa: King's Printer, 1901.

KING, LEWIS H.
*On the Sediments and Stratigraphy
of the Scotian Shelf.*
The Geological Ass'n. of Canada,
Paper No. 4, 1967.

PARADIS, R.
La Géologie de Québec.
Quebec: Department of Mines, 1941-44.

SABINA, ANN P.
Rock and Mineral Collecting in Canada.
(Volume 3, New Brunswick, Nova Scotia,
Prince Edward Island, Newfoundland).
Ottawa: Geological Survey of Canada, 1965.

SABINA, ANN P.
*Rocks and Minerals for the Collector:
Bay of Fundy Area.*
Ottawa: Geological Survey of Canada, 1964.

STOCKWELL, C. H. (ed.)
Geology and Economic Minerals of Canada.
Ottawa: Geological Survey of Canada, 1963.

INDEX

ACKNOWLEDGEMENTS

The author and editors wish to acknowledge with gratitude the advice and assistance of: the officers of the Fisheries Research Board of Canada, the Atlantic Oceanographic Laboratory, Bedford Institute, Dartmouth, N.S., the Canadian Wildlife Service, the Federal Forestry Department, the Geological Survey of Canada; Messrs. Carl Medcof, Wilfred Templeman, A. B. Huntsman, A. C. Kohler, L. M. Dickie, J. E. Paloheimo, F. D. McCracken, W. R. Martin, T. K. Pitt, Hubert Squires, S. N. Tibbo, A. M. Fleming, A. H. Leim, L. R. Day, P. F. Elson, V. M. Hodder, C. J. Kerswill, D. H. Steele, M. W. Smith, D. G. Wilder, D. J. Scarratt, R. E. Drinnan – on salt-water, anadromous and freshwater fish, lobsters, shellfish, etc.; Messrs. I. C. M. Place, R. M. Strang, W. J. Carroll, A. W. H. Damman, Stewart Gage, R. S. Forbes, H. D. Long, R. F. Morris, Murray M. Neilson, Charles Bennet – on forestry and forest entomology; Ron Trites – on oceanography; Ernest Rouleau – on general botany; Messrs. W. H. Poole, Lewis King, G. S. Mackenzie, R. R. Potter, J. C. Smith, B. R. Pelletier – on geology; Messrs. Winston Mair, Bruce Wright, Douglas H. Pimlott, D. E. Sergeant, A. T. Bergerud – on land and marine mammals; Messrs. Austin Squires, Alfred O. Gross, Charles S. Huntington, Stuart S. Peters, Leslie M. Tuck, Peter Pearce – on land and sea birds, migration, etc.; J. B. Sprague – on freshwater pollution; Constance I. MacFarlane – on seaweeds; Dr. F. P. Ide – on mayflies; Rube Hornstein – on climate; Libby Oughton – special research and editing; and many others in the field, fishermen, provincial government officials, game wardens, bird watchers in the Maritimes.

PICTURE CREDITS

Order of appearance in the text of pictures listed here is left to right, top to bottom.

Cover/A. J. Harris
1/Fred Bruemmer
2–3/Rosemary Gilliat
4–5/Franklin Russell
8/Stan Fillmore
10–11/Harold Whyte and Templeton Studios
22/Dr. B. K. Deans
24/M. J. Dodswell
27/John deVisser
29/National Film Board (Stills)
40/Dr. B. K. Deans
47/Dr. George K. Peck
49/John deVisser
53/Wm. H. Amos
64/Dr. D. R. Gunn
70/M. J. Dodswell, B. S. Jackson
71/Cyril F. Smith
73/Rosemary Gilliat
75/Dr. George K. Peck
76/M. J. Dodswell, B. S. Jackson, Dr. George K. Peck, Dr. George K. Peck
77/Wm. H. Amos
78/B. S. Jackson, A. J. Harris
79/Mrs. I. M. Paim, Mrs. I. M. Paim, Wm. H. Amos
80/Wm. H. Amos
81/Cyril F. Smith, Wm. H. Amos, Wm. H. Amos
82/Wm. H. Amos
87/Paul Germain/Fotopol
93/Wm. H. Amos
102/Rosemary Gilliat, Mrs. I. M. Paim, Mrs. I. M. Paim
103/Rosemary Gilliat
104/Dr. George K. Peck, Dr. George K. Peck
105/Dr. George J. Peck, Mrs. I. M. Paim
106/Dr. George K. Peck, Dr. George K. Peck
107/Dr. George K. Peck
117/Mrs. Joan Gunn
118–122/All by Doctor D. R. Gunn except page 121 top right which is by Mrs. Joan Gunn
126–128/Barry Ranford/Format
138/Paul Germain/Fotopol

This book was produced entirely in Canada by
Mono Lino Typesetting Co. Limited: *Typesetting;* Herzig Sommerville Limited: *Film Separation*
Ashton-Potter Limited: *Printing;* T. H. Best Printing Co. Limited: *Binding*
Typefaces: *Times New Roman and Univers.* Paper: *65 lb. Georgian Offset Smooth*
PRINTED IN CANADA

C D E F F 73 72